Did you know...?

The **ADHD Awareness Book Project** is an ongoing effort to bring the best tips and strategies, and now also stories, from the world's top ADHD experts, to you in an easily digestible format. The series includes:

- *365 Ways to Succeed with ADHD (2011)*
- *365+1 Ways to Succeed with ADHD (2012)*
- *More Ways to Succeed with ADHD (2013)*
- *Inspirational Ways to Succeed with ADHD (2014)*

Each book contains unique content and follows a "bite-sized" format for easy reading. By adding all **four Amazon #1 Bestselling** books to your collection, you will have over 1000 unique ADHD strategies and stories at your fingertips! With such a large variety, you are guaranteed to discover a number of tips and/or stories that will make the difference!

This series is the perfect gift for yourself, a loved, or an ADHD professional you know.

Order all four editions at www.CoachingforADHD.com

Praise for the ADHD Awareness Book Project!

"Whether you have ADHD or are supporting someone with ADHD there is something for everyone in The ADHD Awareness Book Project. This series is an excellent resource! There has been a need for this type of book for a long time. Now, it is finally here!!!"

~**David Giwerc,** Founder & President, ADD Coach Academy, author of *Permission to Proceed: The Keys to Creating a Life of Passion, Purpose and Possibility for Adults with ADHD*

"Full of wit and wisdom! Brilliant best tips from some of the best in the field and short enough to be read and appreciated by even those with ADHD who hate to read. Love it!

~**Michelle Novotni,** Ph.D. ADHD Expert; Psychologist and ADHD coach and author of *What Do Other People Know that I Don't*

"I meet all kinds of people with a creeping sense that their attention is out of whack. Laurie's books are perfect for a daily dose of awareness for the diagnosed ADDer, the self-diagnosed, and those who are ADDish or chronically disorganized. You'll love them for both practicality and humor."

~ **Judith Kolberg**, author of *Conquering Chronic Disorganization* and *ADD-Friendly Ways to Organize Your Life,* www.squallpress.net

"Read 365+1 ways to succeed with ADHD, and Laurie's other books, and you'll quickly develop an interesting, new ADHD recovery vocabulary. 'Comprehensive' is one new and essential ADHD evaluation and treatment word. ADHD, as you know, is more complex than a simple set of labels, and treatment/recovery requires a careful review of multiple

issues, many covered in the deeply comprehensive pages of Laurie's books. From my perspective, 365+1 Ways to Succeed with ADHD is the singular most comprehensive ADHD recovery book available, and I strongly encourage you to read and listen to the abundant array of national experts who provided their best insights for your next recovery steps."

~ **Dr. Charles Parker**, Psychiatrist and Psycho-pharmacologist at Core Psych and author of *New ADHD Medication Rules*

"Laurie Dupar has done it again with this new amazing compilation of wisdom from the top experts and practitioners in the field. Just like her first book, this new one is infused with her positive view. Laurie Dupar's devotion to helping people with ADHD live rewarding and strength-based lives is evident. I have her first book in my waiting room, and I frequently see clients pick it up for a few minutes before their appointments, turn randomly to a new page, and always find something that speaks just to them. This new book delivers equally practical wisdom in bite-size pieces. A reader will always find something to help them at the right time in an extremely ADHD friendly format."

~ **Sari Solden**, Psychotherapist, MS, LMFT, and author of *Women with Attention Deficit Disorder* and *Journeys Through ADD*

With much love and appreciation to all of my colleagues. Without your support this book would never have been possible.

Thank you for being my tribe!

~ Laurie Dupar

The ADHD Awareness Book Project

INSPIRATIONAL
Ways to Succeed
with ADHD

REAL LIFE STORIES AND STRATEGIES TO HELP YOU THRIVE WITH ADHD

Laurie Dupar, PMHMP, RN, PCC

INSPIRATIONAL Ways to Succeed with ADHD

ISBN 978-0-692-24013-7

This book is not intended as a substitute for the medical advice of physicians. The reader should regularly consult a physician in matters relating to his/her health and particularly with respect to any symptoms that may require diagnosis or medical attention.

Publisher: Laurie Dupar, Herding Cats Press

Granite Bay, CA

Cover Design by Jodi Burgess Design

Content editing by Liz Ahmann, Writing Rx

About The *ADHD Awareness Book Project*

"Never doubt that a small group of thoughtful, committed, people can change the world. Indeed it is the only thing that ever has."

~Margaret Mead

The ADHD Awareness Book Project began four years ago with these goals: provide people with ADHD valuable strategies and tips to help them succeed and increase the awareness of ADHD world-wide, all in an ADHD-friendly format!

We have come a long way in our understanding of ADHD, considering that in 1902 symptoms consistent with ADHD were labeled a "morbid defect of moral control"! We have come to understand that ADHD is neither gender nor ethnic specific and is not something individuals out-grow. However, the fact that ADHD is a real and lifelong disorder has not yet made enough of an impact on the overall awareness or successful daily management of ADHD symptoms and challenges.

Too often I hear from people all over the world—parents, students and newly diagnosed adults—who are struggling alone, not knowing that answers to their challenges are available. Many have never heard the term 'ADHD' and they have no idea that by learning to do things in ways that better fit their ADHD brain-style, they could succeed . . . at just about anything!

After 11 years of specializing in ADHD, and over 25 years working in mental health, the continued lack of awareness about ADHD, and the limited availability of resources, is no longer acceptable to me. Frankly, I am tired. I am tired of knowing that individuals, from young children to adults in their 70s, are struggling alone with ADHD, unaware that there are answers, resources, hope and help out here. I have decided to be part of the solution by publishing these books, and I am not alone.

Nearly four years ago, believing in the power of community and the dedication of my colleagues in the ADHD community, I announced that I would be coordinating a book of tips and strategies for succeeding with ADHD, featuring as many ADHD experts as possible. I invited all the ADHD professionals I knew, and asked them to invite ADHD professionals they knew, to participate in this project. In the first *ADHD Awareness Book Project,* titled ***365 Ways to Succeed with ADHD***, over

80 co-authors from a variety of professions responded to my request and submitted their answers to the question: "What is the best tip or strategy you have to help someone with ADHD succeed?"

In its second edition, titled ***365+1** Ways to Succeed with ADHD,* the *ADHD Awareness Book Project* expanded to incorporate contributing experts from all over the globe, including South Africa, Turkey, Sweden, Denmark, Ireland, Canada, the U.K. Our experts included 'junior experts', and 'senior experts', like 78-year-olds, sharing their strategies to help people with ADHD succeed.

In its third edition, *MORE Ways to Succeed with ADHD*, we answered the call again for "more". More unique ways, tips, strategies and ideas to help better manage ADHD.

And, in this fourth edition, *Inspirational Ways to Succeed with ADHD*, alongside this year's brand-new tips and strategies, we have added powerful, uplifting stories about ADHD from people just like you. I know that within these pages you will find the one specific tip, strategy or story that will be the answer you are most needing in this moment.

How YOU are making a difference when you buy this book!

Whether this book is for you or for someone you care about, a portion of the sales of *The ADHD Awareness Book Project: Inspirational Ways to Succeed with ADHD* will be used to support three international ADHD organizations:

- Children and Adults with Attention Deficit/Hyperactivity Disorder (CHADD)
- Attention Deficit Disorder Association (ADDA)
- ADHD Coaches Organization (ACO)

Thank you for purchasing this book, being part of the solution, and helping us to increase awareness of ADHD!

~ Laurie Dupar

How to Use this Book

Our books are intended to be 'ADHD friendly.' They are formatted to include a large variety of tips and stories that are short, succinct, easy to read and immediately useable.

Some of you may want to put this book by your bedside and read one tip a day . . . Terrific! Some of you may sit down and read the entire book in one sitting . . . Have fun! Still others, in your very wonderful ADHD style, may thumb through the book, starting wherever it catches your attention, reading from the middle to the end, . . . the end to the middle, . . . or even every other page! It is yours to decide. Enjoy this book in whatever manner your wonderful ADHD brain chooses!

Contact the Contributors

As you read through these pages, and find particular strategies useful, or stories inspiring, I encourage you to connect with the contributors. They look forward to hearing from you!

Contents

Dedication

This book is dedicated to people living with ADHD, wherever you are. Your commitment, perseverance and determination to find answers about how to live successfully with ADHD are a constant source of inspiration. YOU are the experts. YOU are the source for what we know "works" and what, even though it might make sense, doesn't.

This book is also dedicated to ADHD professionals who are committed to making a positive difference in the lives of people with ADHD. These experts include: doctors, therapists, nutritionists and dieticians, coaches, educators, lawyers, accountants, organizing specialists and many more. Many of you chose to share your expertise by contributing to this book. Thank you all. I am proud to be your colleague.

Individually, we make a difference in the lives of people with ADHD. Together, there is the bigger possibility to positively change the world's understanding and awareness of ADHD. This book could not have happened without ALL of you. Thank you.

Acknowledgements

Putting this book together has been a labor of love, borne by a passion to make a positive difference in the lives of people with ADHD. In fact, I can say it has been with an 'ADHD spirit' that for the past four years, the books of *The ADHD Awareness Book Project* have been written and published. Four years ago I had an idea, and I was determined to make it a reality without thought to any obstacles, roadblocks, nay-sayers or disbelievers. Fore-most in my thoughts has always been you, the people I both have met and have yet to meet who live with ADHD.

With you always on my mind, I was determined to do what someone with ADHD would do: find a way through the obstacles, keep an eye on the goal despite its seeming impossibility, and get up each day determined and hopeful to succeed. You are the inspiration. Thank you.

I also want to thank all of the contributors of *The ADHD Awareness Book Project: Inspirational Ways to Succeed with ADHD.* Your individual and collective beliefs, support as well as contributions to this book have made it a reality. I am humbled by your commitment.

And, of course, I want to thank my family: you know

who you are. Without your constant belief in me, and your un-dying patience, this effort would not have been possible. I love you all.

I also want to thank my assistant extraordinaire, Meg Gehan, who always has my back; Shaun Roney, who is a master at managing my media; Jodi Burgess at Jodi Burgess Design, who created the book cover; and Liz Ahmann at Writing Rx, whose expertise and craft with words helped all of our entries 'sparkle.' This wouldn't have been possible without each and all of you. Thank you!

~Laurie Dupar

Introduction

Fourteen years ago, my youngest son was diagnosed with ADHD. As a mental health professional used to having the answers, I uncharacteristically found myself searching for anything that would help me better understand this mental health disorder so that I could help him minimize his challenges and maximize his talents. At the time, resources were scarce. Several years later, I discovered ADHD coaching and saw how much of a difference this approach made in helping both of us reduce the struggles and, instead, experience success. Surprising even myself, becoming an ADHD coach and working with people having unique brain styles as they tap into their brilliance, has been my passion for the past 11 years. And my son? He is proudly pursuing his dream of serving in the United States Navy.

I never set out to be an ADHD coach. Having earned my master's degree as a psychiatric mental health nurse practitioner, I was prepared to diagnose and treat the whole array of mental health disorders. I would have never believed that understanding, advocating for or working with people diagnosed with ADHD would have been so all-consuming and rewarding. Yet, I have been amazed with the never-slowing stream of people challenged with this disorder. As an ADHD coach, I get to work with some of the most amazingly brilliant and creative people every day . . . and these are just my clients. The experts, professionals and specialists who focus on working with people diagnosed with ADHD are equally as incredible.

ADHD is a 24/7 disorder impacting the ability of affected individuals to focus, pay attention, plan, prioritize . . . and a whole host of other challenges. For some people with ADHD, it is difficult to complete less interesting tasks like homework, bills, organizing or planning. The inability to complete these tasks often creates huge disorder and chaos in their lives. For others, throughout the day, from the moment of waking to the hours of trying to fall asleep, daily life can be a struggle, whether to find motivation or to fight distractions due to an inner sense of restlessness. That's the thing about ADHD . . . . It is so different for everyone.

A number of amazing international organizations are available to help people better understand ADHD. I am proud that a portion of the proceeds of the book sales of *The ADHD Awareness Book Project* goes to support these organizations. I encourage you to seek out the resources of such organizations as Children and Adults with Attention Deficit Disorder (CHADD), www.chadd.org; Adults with Attention Deficit Disorder Association (ADDA), www.add.org; and the ADHD Coaches Organization (ACO), www.adhdcoaches.org

In addition, many books are available by authors who really understand the challenges of ADHD, some of whom have contributed to this book. I encourage you to explore their wisdom. I believe we can never know too much about ADHD.

And last, but not least, there are individual professionals who serve the ADHD community. Coaches, doctors, researchers, therapists, nutritionists, educators, lawyers, and others. Over the years, I have been awed at this community's dedication and commitment to serve, each individual, each using unique strengths, talents and gifts, each in his or her own way, to improve the lives of people with ADHD.

Inspirational Ways to Succeed with ADHD is our fourth book. The first book, ***365 Ways to Succeed with ADHD***, the second, ***365+1 Ways to Succeed with ADHD*** and the third, ***MORE ways to Succeed with ADHD*** each achieved a #1 ranking in their category on Amazon.com. We hope this book will be a #1 resource for you as well!

The ADHD Awareness Book Project has been an opportunity for many experts to come together in one place to share their 'gems' with you. It is written with parents, families, children, teachers, teens, college students and adults of all ages in mind. There is literally something for everyone!

Drawing from their wide varieties of expertise and experience, contributing experts have offered you their best strategies and tips to help you succeed with ADHD. I know you will enjoy and find value in all of their contributions.

"I will keep telling you

that you are important,

deserving, loving, intelligent,

worthy, compassionate,

beautiful, creative, inspiring,

brave, true, strong, and able

until you finally

realize it for yourself."

~Anonymous

Getting Things Done, 15 Minutes at a Time

Do you struggle to complete mundane, tedious, or boring tasks? Make these tasks more interesting and more manageable by scheduling them as 15 minute "sprints". Gather all the needed supplies, set a timer, and get to work. Once you get started, you may find the motivation you need to keep working. If not, that's okay! Even if a task requires multiple sprints, knowing that you only have to spend 15 minutes at a time makes it seem more manageable. You can also make a game out of it by trying to see how much you can accomplish before the timer goes off. This little trick is great for kids, especially when it is time to clean up. Challenge them to get as much cleaned up as possible before the timer goes off. Make sure you acknowledge their efforts when they're done!

~ Ally Martin

Ally Martin, ADHD coach, and founder of Attention Solutions, specializes in teens and adults with ADHD. Contact her at: www.attention-solutions.com Ally@attention-solutions.com

Be the Star of Your Story

We've all been told something about ourselves that we've come to believe over time. Perhaps you were told many times that you're a dramatic person (even if you always saw yourself as passionate). If you hear "you're dramatic" over and over, you start to believe it and may even have started fulfilling the role. This can all happen without you ever realizing it. As people with ADHD, we've probably been called everything in the book . . . from unreliable to hyper to impulsive. Guess what? Those are other people's stories about you . . . your story is your own. You're the writer. Your perspective of yourself is an active choice that you alone must make. The way you frame your life and what you choose to emphasize will change how you live your life. Don't play a role in someone else's story about you – be the star of your own story!

~ Dr. Billi Bittan, MA, PhD, ADHD Specialist, NeuroCognitive Behavioral Therapist and Coach

Dr. Billi, PhD, ADHD Specialist, NeuroCognitive Behavioral/Expressive Arts Therapist/Coach. Reframe Your Narrative, Change Your Life, Leverage ADHD to Your ADDvantage. www.AttentionB.com DrBilli@AttentionB.com (855) Dr-Billi

You May Have ADHD If...

An ADHD diagnosis is helpful, but it's important to remember that everyone's ADHD shows up differently. You may have ADHD if you . . .

- are a daydreamer
- are distracted easily
- live in the present moment
- have one speed—either very fast or sluggishly slow
- find that people cannot keep up with your thinking
- are much better at work that you are interested in
- can stay up all night if you find a book or game interesting enough
- have trouble dividing a task into steps and estimating how long each step will take
- often take twice, or even three times, longer than you expected to complete things
- often misplace things
- have a cluttered room or household
- see everything as a priority
- typically procrastinate
- need time to process before making decisions
- tend to be a perfectionist
- are distracted by squirrels ;-)

~ Jenny Bandyk, ADHD Coach

Jenny Bandyk, ADHD Coach and consultant, encourages others to understand and ADDentify their own unique ADHD from a strengths based perspective. Contact her at info@ADDentifier.com or visit www.ADDentifier.com

Reframe Your Narrative, Change Your Life

We know we cannot change history – the past is in the past. But we *can* change our perspective of it. If something from your past is holding you back, it's time to reframe it. You can either be a victim or a hero in your story. The choice is yours. So choose to be the hero. Perhaps someone or something specific affected you in the past. Write a story about it. You can even write a letter directly to the person. Write from the perspective of the place you're in now. You don't have to mail it – simply writing it down will give you greater understanding of your story. From here, decide how to reframe your story, how you can release the blame or shame in your past. The goal is to reframe your past, not change it, so you can change your present mindset and create a bright, sustainable future.

~ Dr. Billi Bittan, MA, PhD, ADHD Specialist,
NeuroCognitive Behavioral Therapist and Coach

Dr. Billi, PhD, ADHD Specialist, Neuro-Cognitive Behavioral/Expressive Arts Therapist/Coach. Reframe Your Narrative, Change Your Life, Leverage ADHD to Your ADDvantage. www.AttentionB.com DrBilli@AttentionB.com (855) Dr-Billi

Parenting from Desperation to Inspiration

I call it my Scarlet O'Hara moment, which is kind of ironic for a southern feminist like me. But my story is full of contradictions, so it fits.

Alone for a moment on a family camping weekend, I wanted to scream from the tent-tops, "She's going to be okay – and so am I!" Thankfully, I restrained myself! The moment was filled with tears of pure joy and sheer determination.

What does Scarlet O'Hara have to do with raising children with complex needs? O'Hara's sheer determination inspired me. I raised my fist and spoke aloud to no one, "As God is my witness, no parent should ever again go through, alone, what I've gone through these last 10 years!" Parenting from inspiration like that can be pretty powerful.

Shameful Secrets

My shameful little secret: The first ten years as a parent I was miserable.

Despite passionately loving my kids, pouring my heart and soul (and every waking moment) into giving them opportunities, it was ten long years of being a "Lost Mom":

isolation, confusion, conflicting diagnoses, incredible uncertainty.

My newborn began to scream at 2 weeks old, which set the stage for the decade to come. When her peers were going to karate and ballet, she went to occupational therapy and vision therapy. When her classmates were exploring friendships and learning to spend-the-night out, she changed schools, and then changed again.

It was incredibly unsettling. I watched longingly as parents of other "complex" kids found common ground with each other. They diagnosed challenges, shared, learned, and helped each other move out of denial and into acceptance. I wanted that sense of community so much. But my daughter seemed more complicated. It wasn't just ADHD, or anxiety, or learning disabilities – it was all of it combined.

Alone on a Tightrope without a Net

For me, parenting was like walking onto a tightrope, watching as my safety net was removed, and continuing on without a net, uncertain whether there would be a safe landing on the other side.

It was terrifying out there on the wire. The crowd was watching. There was no turning back. I felt incredibly responsible and unbelievably irresponsible. I had no confidence, no safety-net of 'typical child'. Worse yet, there was a child on my shoulders.

And the only safety net for that child was me.

Fear dominated my life for a decade. With no previous parenting experience, no mentor as my guide, I was shocked to have a child who was so full of contradictions – bright, but out of sync; verbal, but socially awkward; capable, but unable to master simple life skills.

I was desperate for guidance for myself, desperate for the "answers" to help my child. My child's therapist was great for her, but I needed support to help me to feel calm and confident. I wanted OUT of that constant feeling of DESPERATION, to replace it with something constructive for everyone! I didn't know where to turn.

From Desperation to Inspiration

If I have learned one thing above all else in my second decade of parenting, it's this:

You cannot effectively parent from a place of desperation.

Inspiration came when I understood and accepted my child as she was, and planned for her possibilities, instead of only seeing her deficits. It came when I looked outside of the lens of my own panic and saw my child's true potential.

Inspiration is about creating possibilities. And it's all about you, not your child.

My fist triumphantly in the air, I stood in the woods and celebrated that my daughter could have a fulfilling life. With support, I could help her get there – even though I didn't know how. It was exhilarating, holding hope for her – and for me!

My transformation from desperation to inspiration was sparked by three things:

- my own diagnosis at age 40 (which made my whole life make sense)
- a nutritionist who showed me that little changes can have BIG impact
- a coach who held my hand across the virtual tight-rope to safety

It is difficult to raise complex kids, and to overcome isolation, years of not knowing, and uncertainty. It's hard to feel confident when you're not on solid ground. But nothing can get you to solid ground faster and more effectively than INSPIRATION. Believing in your child. Believing in yourself. That's the golden ticket.

Armed with new understanding and a new sense of hope, I went back to school, became a certified coach, and pledged to provide a touchstone for all those parents who feel lost and desperate. Never again would a parent feel isolated and alone like I had. Not on my watch.

Most of us start this parenting journey inspired, but one walk out onto a high-wire – whatever it is for you – can send you spiraling out of confidence. Remember, you are not alone on that wire. Inspiration & support will get you back down to safety!

~ Elaine Taylor-Klaus, CPCC, PCC, co-founder ImpactADHD®

Elaine Taylor-Klaus, CPCC, PCC, is the mother of 3 "complex" children, a graduate of Wesleyan University, CT and the CORO Fellows program, a certified Co-Active Coach, public speaker and writer, and the co-founder of ImpactADHD®. She provides training, coaching and support for parents at all stages of managing "complex" kids. ImpactADHD fulfills Elaine's lifelong mission to make a difference in the world, especially in the lives of women and their families. ImpactADHD programs provide guidance for parents online and on the phone, including videos, home study courses, and group and individual coaching. Read more from Elaine on ImpactADHD.com or at www.HuffingtonPost.com/Elaine-TaylorKlaus/

What is Your External Memory?

How do you keep track of those zillions of thoughts spinning around in your head? If you are like most people with creative, idea-generating ADHD brains, keeping track of all of these thoughts is a challenge. The truth is, your brain is built for idea-generating, not for remembering details.

An "external memory" is something outside of our own brains that we use to help us remember things more easily. For some, the smart phone calendar is the "external memory," or it could be the "notes" feature, or some other useful app. For others, a friend, relative or assistant may keep track of and remind them of ideas, plans, and appointments. Then again, some happily use the old-fashioned paper planner, calendar or organizer.

Whatever your external memory system is, using it consistently, and referring to it daily (or even hourly), is key!

~ Laurie Dupar, PMHNP, RN, PCC

Laurie Dupar is an internationally recognized ADHD coach and thought leader in the ADHD community. Visit her website to find more useful strategies: www.CoachingforADHD.com

Begin at the Beginning

People with ADHD sometimes have trouble starting tasks. If you . . .

- Put things off until the last minute
- Find it difficult to set aside a preferred activity
- Don't know how to get started
- Have a hard time following routines
- Feel unmotivated
- Don't start tasks unless you fully understand them
- Have difficulty writing a paper
- Are told that you're lazy . . .

. . . more than likely you have challenges with the part of your brain that helps with task initiation.

Strengthen your brain's "executive function" skill of task initiation by using the following plan: BEGIN

B - Break task into smaller steps.
E - Establish a schedule.
G - Gadgets to trigger your start time are key.
I - Incentives (a preferred activity) when finished help.
N - Natural consequence work (e.g., eat vegetables, then eat dessert)

Now, go start that personal revolution you've been dreaming about!

~Laurie Moore Skillings, SCAC

Laurie Moore Skillings, Senior Certified ADHD Coach, teaches you how to focus on the task at hand. Email Laurie: support@focuswithease.com

Lazy Susan Homework

Do you find that asking your child to sit down and pay attention doesn't work to get homework done? You might want to try the "Lazy Susan Homework" method!

Clear a large space in which your child will do homework. It might be a dining table, a bed or the floor. Make sure there is plenty of room for your child to move around.

Next, have your child arrange the homework assignments by putting different pieces at different "stations" around the area. It might be that the science project is at the head of the table, and math is at the other end.

Finally, have your child set a timer for, say, 10 minutes and start anywhere . . . it doesn't matter where. When the timer rings, have your child move to the next station and reset the timer to begin the new subject, project, or task.

Continue to move around, resetting the timer, until all the homework is complete!

~Laurie Dupar, PHMNP, RN, PCC

Laurie Dupar is an internationally recognized ADHD expert, coach, author, speaker and fierce advocate for the ADHD community. Connect with her at: www.coachingforadhd.com

Smile a Little Smile for Me

"Christina" was a client of mine who believed that a bachelor's degree from a well-known college would be the ticket to the perfect job. But the job she had as an administrative assistant in a busy office was killing her. She was asked to multi-task all day: to answer phones, greet people coming in the door, direct traffic, and when she wasn't doing all that, write analytical reports for her boss.

For someone with ADHD, her job might seem to be a good fit. After all, how could you get bored doing so many things at once? But it was multi-tasking with *mundane chores* that created the problem. You see, Christina did best when she could do meaningful work, such as the report writing for her boss. When visitors came into the office, she became aggravated when she had to switch from "professional writer" to "greeter." What she really wanted to say was, "Excuse me, I'm working on these calculations for my spreadsheet – I'm not in social mode right now." She also needed a few seconds to stop what she was doing, refocus her thoughts, get into the "friendly" mindset, and then greet visitors with a smile. Christina explained, "I didn't value the small talk. Being task oriented, the interruptions were bothersome. When hyperfocusing on the report, I couldn't switch gears so quickly. My ADHD was getting the best of me! Consequently, I was perceived as indifferent and unwelcoming by my coworkers and visitors. At one point, someone even called me a cold bitch!" Christina was eventually put on warning by her boss, who wanted her to be friendlier and to smile more often.

One day, in frustration, Christina's boss moved her to a back room away from the public; it was there that Christina found her niche. "I loved being away from the loud radio in the reception area and away from people making small talk and interrupting my work," she stated. Being in a quiet place allowed her to concentrate and focus on her long term projects. In no time at all, Christina's report writing became the template for the entire agency. She received accolades from several departments regarding both her work *and* her efficiency. She quickly moved upward in the company and within a month had her own office and was training others, writing policies, and researching for the organization.

Christina, now in her distraction-free office, not only did her work well, but, in addition, her creativity blossomed. "I was able to take my work to an entirely new level which I never had imagined when I was in the front office," she said. "Being able to hyperfocus allowed me to see the possibilities of what else could be done with my reports." She added, "Simply being in the right environment was key. With my ADHD, too much stimuli was overwhelming. The mundane tasks had no purpose for me. I now know I need to control my environment and have a quiet place to work. I know, too, that multi-tasking kills my creative processing, so I avoid that as well." Christina's report writing is now based on her own research, not someone else's. And office-mates come to her for help and guidance.

"I recently had my yearly evaluation," Christina remarked, "and I received outstanding marks in every category. My boss has recommended me for a raise along with a new title – one that is designed just for me and the work I am doing for the company."

And the biggest change of all, her boss notes, is that Christina smiles all the time, never be looked at as indifferent or unwelcoming again.

~ Barbara Ryan Hausman

Barbara Ryan Hausman, coordinator of learning and disability services at DeSales University, is an ADHD coach specializing in the impact of ADHD on the college student. Barbara coaches students in how to integrate their strengths and interests to increase performance and success, not only in college, but in all aspects of life. She is a contributing author of *More Ways to Succeed with ADHD* (2013), compiled and edited by Laurie Dupar. Hausman can be reached at Barbara.hausman@desales.edu

Practice Brain Dumping to Regain Control, Peace and Joy!

Living in today's busy world floods our minds with information, making it difficult to sort out the important from the unimportant. With ADHD, the fact that you might be more easily overwhelmed does not help.

When overwhelmed, we need to clear our brain's bandwidth by getting that excess of information out of our heads and down on paper. To "brain dump," we can use the visual structure of mind mapping:

Grab a large piece of paper and colored pens. Draw a circle in the middle, and write in it your name or "me." Dump/write names of your projects and worries in circles surrounding the center circle. For example, write "book project", "find a new accountant" and "declutter working space" in separate circles. This visual scheme will make it easier to start identifying priorities as well as dramatically reduce the feeling of anxiety and overwhelm.

~ Anna Maria Lindell, ADHD-coach, speaker and founder of Advance LP AB

Anna Maria Lindell, ADHD Coach, specializes in helping entrepreneurs and other high achievers with ADHD traits better understand their brains, and increase their productivity. www.advancesweden.se

Surprise! ADHD

Hopelessness.

Surprise! Bet you didn't think anyone in this book would tell you to embrace hopelessness or, put differently, look for an opportunity to just give up.

This is sounding interesting now, right?

But giving up is how to beat the ADHD perfectionism trap. That brain-freezing, stuck, no oxygen feeling when you are thinking there is ONE RIGHT WAY to do something and you don't know what that one way is.

So when is it okay to embrace "I can't"? When:

- We are trying to be perfect.
- We are trying to please everyone.
- We are trying to avoid every conflict.
- We think we can get it all done today.
- We think we can say "yes" to whatever someone asks us to do.
- We ____________________. (Your turn to fill in here.)

~ Catherine Pietrow, Certified ADHD Coach

Catherine Pietrow is a Certified ADHD Coach who loves her work with teens and adults to discover their strengths, tap into their best selves, and shoot for the stars, all while keeping a sense of humor (845) 702-8329

The Gift of Hyperfocus...?!

I've heard it said: "Do what you love, and love what you do." Well, isn't this the essence of ADHD hyper-focusing? If you or someone you know has experienced "locking in" to a subject of interest to the point that it is the only thing you do (or want to do) for an extended period of time, you will know that hyperfocus has its pros and cons. Hyperfocus is gratifying and fun, yet it can take time away from other essential tasks needing attention.

Less often considered is whether there are times when hyperfocus can be seen not only as fun, but actually as a gift.

During my 7th grade year, I took Spanish for the first time. Little did I know that hyperfocus on Spanish would impact its use into my post-graduate career and adult life.

My teacher, Señora Pritz from Brazil, was loud, colorful and fast-speaking, and she demanded participation from her pupils. Before entering our class every day, we had to answer a vocabulary question or sound out a word. She had us chanting the vowel sounds together and singing ABBA songs in Spanish.

Well, my ADHD brain and auditory learning style just loved it! I couldn't get enough. So much so that I started pronouncing English words and phrases in Spanish, even at home! I mean, I used a Spanish twist on everything: menus, billboards, friends and family members' names (which they found quite annoying, apparently), movie credits and more.

Needless to say, I did well in Spanish that year, which encouraged me to continue learning it, all the way through college. I took study-abroad trips and went on to practice as a bilingual school psychologist for many years. Native speakers have commented on my Spanish "accent": they usually ask me when and where I studied! Well, I attribute my success to my initial hyper-focus on the language, enjoying the "pronunciation game" everywhere I went.

So, stop and notice what you, your student, or your spouse gets hyper-focused on. When you are doing what you love, and loving what you are doing, there is purpose and a reason, even if it may not seem relevant in the moment. Consider that there just might be something in that particular activity or behavior that, if developed and honed, will be important, meaningful or purposeful later on down the road.

My advice? Accept and appreciate "ADHDness" and encourage the positives that can come from its hyper-focusing and other traits...en Inglés, Español o qualquier idioma!

~ Melissa Fahrney, MA, ACC, CSS

Coach Melissa Fahrney holds a master's degree in psychology and certifications in both life and ADHD coaching for children, teens and adults. She is also a certified Career Services Specialist, licensed HeartMath™ coach, and meditation teacher. Fahrney has worked as a bilingual (Spanish) school psychologist. Providing stress management training, career development and ADHD education to her coaching clients via phone or online, she helps individuals, families and groups achieve successful balance, productivity and FUN. Being in NW Montana, she enjoys outdoor recreation year-round with her family. Contact Melissa: 1coachmelissa@gmail.com, www.addheartworks.com

"There are so many

people out there who

will tell you that you can't.

What you've got to do

is turn around and say

"Watch me!"

~Anonymous

Recruit Your Ultimate Tribe

My dad's mother and sisters were big personalities who expressed opinions freely, expecting the same from everyone else. Mom found them intimidating (and likely couldn't form a cogent thought in their company). I saw them infrequently. Yet, now, I'm drawn to women like these.

If a woman invites and listens to alternate viewpoints, resists using debate as sport, and can be vulnerable, I'll move closer. However, if she loves debate and banter, I've learned that I'll be tired and foggy-brained soon. I can enjoy her, but being rather permeable, I won't embed her into my "Tribe." And . . . she likely would design hers without me!

Your "Tribe" won't look like mine or anyone else's. It reflects *you*. I suggest you include as needed: a coach, therapist, other ADHDers, and someone with whom you connect while differing in style preferences.

Have fun recruiting!

~ Sherri Dettmer Cannon

Sherri Cannon, certified Executive and ADHD Coach, helps you understand, communicate and leverage your strengths! See: www.sherricannon.com sherri@sherricannon.com (310) 548-3623

Synchronized Rhythms

I love to dance, especially to drumming! Perhaps it's because drumming is a tradition from my Latin roots . . . and from many other cultures—African, Asian, Celtic and Nordic. Native Americans believe the drum is the sacred beat of Mother Earth's heart.

Drumming lessons have been challenging and rewarding for me *and* have helped my ADHD. I can almost feel new neural pathways being created as I learn the rhythmic patterns. In fact, research shows that rhythm develops communication, intuition and awareness. It synchronizes the logical left and the intuitive right hemispheres of the brain, in a similar way to practicing meditation. Rhythm stimulates the middle pre-frontal cortex, promoting insight into ourselves and helping us understand others.

My enthusiasm for drumming surpasses my talent. Still, I'm appreciative of how it's not only helped my ADHD symptoms, but also provided great fun!

~ Angelis Iglesias

Angelis Iglesias, ADHD ASD Coach, concentrates on helping adults with ADHD mind traits and parents and caretakers of kids with ADHD. ai@mindheartcoach.org mindheartcoach.org
(512) 777- 1634

Let Freedom Ring, *Not* the Phone!

Many things happen during the day that can distract us, preventing us from accomplishing our priorities. Answering calls every time the phone rings is a common and frequent distractor!

To have a more productive day, try these four simple steps:

1. **Don't answer your phone.** Seriously! When your phone rings, think of it as someone else's priority, not yours. With caller ID, texting, answering machines and voice mail, you really won't miss an important message.

2. **Instead, let the "machine" answer.** If you are worried you'll miss an emergency call from a loved-one, design an alert system ahead of time, such as calling twice in a row.

3. Even better, **set your phone(s) on silent,** and turn off the vibration feature, during your key productivity times.

4. Finally, **decide and plan ahead of time when you will listen to messages** and return calls.

Following these steps puts your chosen priorities back on top of your schedule where they belong!

~Laurie Dupar, PMHNP, RN, PCC

Laurie Dupar is an internationally recognized ADHD coach and thought leader in the ADHD community. Visit her website to find more useful strategies: www.CoachingforADHD.com .

ADHD at Midlife: Reflections

If there's anything worse than ADHD, it's ADHD at midlife!

I know . . . . I've been there. After traveling the ADHD road as a teen, and then into my 20s, 30s, and 40s, I found myself at midlife and in need of life re-invention.

The tendency of those of us with ADHD is to bounce from one thing to another, much as a bee flits from flower to flower. But once we hit midlife, it's more important than ever to get a more clear focus in our lives and define ourselves and our direction.

In my case, this required lots of soul-searching and, ultimately, a total life reinvention. But the good news is that I've discovered powerful tools along the way—not just to help myself, but, now, to use in helping others as a Midlifestyle Reinvention Coach.

~ Mary Buchan, RN, BSN

Mary Buchan, Midlifestyle RNventor and author of the book *Over iT*, helps women who feel stuck discover and align with their life's purpose. www.marybuchan.com

Shame: Secret and Disabling

"I told you that I was frustrated, but how did you guess I might be ashamed?" a client with ADHD recently asked, acknowledging an emotion many prefer to ignore.

"James" had been telling me how his struggles with procrastination had gotten him behind on some work projects. In the course of discussing his "procrastination", he had described his trouble starting various projects because he often feels over-whelmed at the work involved in doing as good a job as he knows he can.

On a logical level, I could have argued that just getting the work done would be better than trying to do the perfect job. James understood that argument . . . and had actually told himself that many times. But, he was still stuck. So, why?

Shame!

Shame is often a secret emotion hiding under other feelings, including frustration and embarrassment, and it is not uncommon among individuals with ADHD.

Shame translates as "I am no good." Not "It's not good that I am getting these projects finished late." No. Shame is deeper, and fear based: "I am no good. I am not worthy."

In her book *The Gifts of Imperfection*, researcher and author Dr. Brené Brown defines shame as follows: "Shame is the intensely painful feeling or experience of believing that we are flawed and therefore unworthy of love and belonging."

Shame hurts!

But you are not alone if you experience shame. We all have it: shame is a primitive human emotion. And for individuals with ADHD, it can be heightened.

At the same time, if we don't acknowledge and address it, shame can become a serious problem, getting in the way of happiness, forward movement, embracing ourselves, and living a full life.

After acknowledging the shame he held inside, my client James decided to spend the week noticing how many times, and when, he gave himself negative messages such as "You aren't good enough," "You don't write well," "You'll never get that finished," "You've never been able to get things done on time," "You shouldn't do it that way," . . . and so forth.

It's important to notice feelings of shame and to notice, as well, the negative messages we may give ourselves. That awareness is the first step in creating a new way forward.

~ Elizabeth (Liz) Ahmann, ScD, RN, ACC

Liz Ahmann is a certified, experienced ADHD coach working with students and others to identify strengths, pinpoint challenges, clarify goals, develop strategies, and support success. Offering tele-classes in mindfulness for ADHD. To learn more, see www.lizahmann.com and www.lizahmann.blogspot.com

Couples & ADHD: Being Perfectly Imperfect

In relationships impacted by ADHD, daily slip-ups and emotional collisions are going to occur. Accepting this fact, and adopting a neutral stance toward your partner's imperfections, can do wonders.

As the ADHD partner, remain open to the idea that you will make mistakes, forget things, and not always recall events perfectly. When disagreements arise, if you view your non-ADHD partner as being critical, your natural response will be to become defensive and retaliatory, making it difficult to solve problems and find cooperative solutions. Instead of feeling criticized, stay open and creative, allowing solutions to come more quickly and easily.

As the partner without ADHD, stay as neutral and positive as possible when giving feedback about something that did not go as planned. Additionally, the simple act of stating even a single positive observation to your partner can change the entire outcome of an otherwise tense situation.

~ Sarah A. Ferman, LMFT, MBA, PsyD &
Robert M. Wilford, PhD

Leading ADHD couples experts, Dr. Ferman & Dr. Wilford, provide solutions to enhance, rebuild and reconnect ADHD couples to create loving, joy filled relationships. www.ADHDCouplesSuccess.com

Do You Brush Your Teeth?

Yes . . . that's right . . . do you brush your teeth? This question may seem random in a strategy book for ADHD, but whether or not you brush your teeth is a good indicator of your ability to learn other new habits.

Think about it. Brushing our teeth is not a natural act. It neither keeps us safe from predators nor provides any nutritional sustenance. Hand-eye coordination is required to do it properly. It takes time, and it requires organizing several items—water, toothpaste and toothbrush. Yet, despite all of this, most of us eventually learn to complete brushing our teeth on a daily basis.

Tooth brushing is a great example of how, with consistent practice, we can learn a new behavior or habit.

So, the next time you feel discouraged, and wonder if you can learn a new habit, ask yourself, "Did I brush my teeth today?" And, there's your answer!

~Laurie Dupar, PMHNP, RN, PCC

Laurie Dupar is an internationally recognized ADHD expert, coach, author, speaker and fierce advocate for the ADHD community. Connect with her at: www.coachingforadhd.com

Finding My Own True Voice . . . Again!

Have you ever felt so terrific that everything, and I mean everything, felt just as it should be, whether you planned it or not? Those are the times when you are not stressed, you are not worried, and you feel like you are in the "flow" of life.

When I was 10, I found myself "in flow"—though I did not recognize it then—when singing. Singing was a wonderful experience that gave me so much joy. It started when I went to camp in the summers. I absolutely loved singing the camp songs. Later, I sang camp songs in the car on the way to family vacation spots. Though other siblings would sometimes join in, it was my mother who really encouraged me and enjoyed the fact that I knew all the words. She loved to sing as well. After a while, my siblings would tire of my singing, and eventually I would stop.

During high school, I babysat for kids who loved to play and sing Broadway musical songs, so we would sing the night away, and I always felt sad when those evenings ended.

At that time, my Church was progressive in allowing use of contemporary folk instruments at masses, so I sang while a friend of mine played guitar. And at my high school I sang in the glee club, loving every minute of it. My last year in high school, I took voice as an elective and learned that I was good at speaking to a large class. I was also told that my facial expressions were very dramatic, sometimes emphatic, and teachers would comment that I was "making a face"! What on earth did they mean? Obviously, I was naïve about how I appeared to others, but I wondered why some people seemed to think I was being rude.

Later, in college, as a drama major, my first acting teacher told me that I had a pleasant speaking voice. Still, I never picked up on the fact that maybe my voice was one of my talents that I should pursue. By this time, I had long forgotten my childhood days of singing, the enjoyment I derived from it, and the happiness and contentment as well.

In my early adult years, my voice was helpful in teaching, and ugly in disciplining. Though I did not sing very often at that time, I was occasionally asked to sing in friends' and relatives' weddings. Surprisingly, I never saw this as an expression of myself. Furthermore, at family gatherings, reunions, when out to dinner, and in public places, I was often told to "tone it down." Even my mother told me that my voice was too loud in conversations: "Shhh . . . ." If I ever spoke up about a matter, it seemed others perceived me as shouting from the rooftops, and, clearly, I was not. What I consider my normal vocal volume, others consider too loud!

How could my voice, something that gave me great joy, peace and contentment, also be so "bad"? The answer is this: the gift of my voice is one of my greatest strengths. I had never realized it before. It was buried treasure. I had simply pushed away the obvious, and tried to focus on the 'shoulds', instead of the self that has always been here.

I no longer bury the treasure that is my gift. I look forward to feeling satisfaction, success, and happiness from my gift once again. Thus, when I think about changing careers now, in the winter of my life, I consider broadcasting, singing, speaking and voice acting! My voice has been excavated for good: I have found my voice . . . again and forever.

~ Katie Blum Katz, ADHD Coach-in-Training, MA, BA, SecEDUC, Certified by ACE

Katie Katz, MA in Dance Educ., Certified K-12 Teacher, ACE Certified Group Fitness, Zumba, & Master Phone Coach, currently a Coach-in-Training with ADDCA, is passionate about coaching and helping individuals with ADHD manage their daily lives. Previously, she coached individuals in their exercise and eating programs. Now with www.Katkoaching.com, she brings a whole new level to Katkoaching. She has developed "Tools you Can Use" for anyone dealing with ADHD challenges. www.Katkoachingcom katie@katkoaching.com
(410) 757-8830

When Your "Go-To" Strategies Have Done Gone!

Strategies I developed in elementary school and perfected into college failed me at 48. The tools that had served me so well? . . . Work harder and stay longer! Being acknowledged for my dedication and hard work was a source of pride, and, ironically, I was promoted at work based on that tenacity and dedication.

But after my last promotion, my tools "work harder and stay longer" left me. I couldn't do it any longer. I was sick, tired and miserable. Life had to change or I would die, not only figuratively but also literally.

My choice? To find ways to leverage time and resources based on my own needs and priorities. Rejecting my old strategies allowed me to discover and appreciate my uniqueness and talents, and launched me into a career that helps others to design lives of their own making, too.

~ DeShawn Wert, BS, MEd, ADHD Coach

DeShawn Wert, BS, MEd, ADHD Coach and consultant. Ready to leverage your strengths to find your answers? Contact: www.youraddanswers.com/services/

Me and My ADHD

My first grade teacher wrote on my report card that I tended to daydream. My dad was my t-ball coach and would put me in far right field because he knew I often wasn't paying attention to the ball. I was a playful, thoughtful girl who wasn't afraid of being herself and sometimes being in her own world. At that age, no one suspected I had ADHD.

In my later college years I first heard about ADHD, but then it was largely associated with hyperactive young boys. I graduated in four years, but now, looking back, I see how many of my academic challenges were related to ADHD. It would have been helpful to know then just a little bit of what I know now about ADHD.

After college, I went to graduate school and began living on my own for the first time. Time management and organization related to studying and due dates were often a challenge. But, still, I did not recognize these as symptoms of ADHD.

After graduate school, I was ready to put my knowledge and skills to work. I worked very hard, yet over the years, at times of high stress, and when juggling multiple projects, I had some work performance issues. Eventually, my supervisor essentially asked what was wrong with me that caused the performance issues. I didn't know. I did experience times of depression, but it was only more recently that I got a diagnosis of ADHD.

In fact, my real understanding of ADHD unfolded at the 2013 Attention Deficit Disorder Association (ADDA) Conference in Detroit, MI. I feel extraordinarily fortunate and thankful that a friend mentioned this conference to me. At the conference I finally came to understand myself and my past struggles and, equally wonderful, I found my "tribe."

My life purpose is now to increase ADHD awareness and, as a coach, to be professionally available to others affected by ADHD.

~ Jenny Bandyk, ADHD Coach

Jenny Bandyk is an ADHD coach and consultant who supports and encourages others to understand and ADDentify their own unique ADHD patterns from a strengths based perspective. She helps individuals and families better understand how ADHD can show up differently across the life span and in varied contexts. Jenny has a master's degree in child development and family studies. She also is an experienced social science, mental health and survey researcher who uses this knowledge to inform her ADHD awareness and coaching endeavors. For more information, please contact her via email at info@ADDentifier.com or visit www.ADDentifier.com

Couples & ADHD: Keeping the Spark Alive In Your Relationship

If at first you don't succeed, give it a little more effort and you might be pleasantly surprised!

When initiating intimacy with your ADHD partner, you might find some initial resistance. This initial lack of interest should be expected given how the ADHD mind works. For partners with ADHD, getting started can seem overwhelming. Until the neurons of interest are firing, the ADHD mind is simply not engaged.

Think about it: how many times have you had to work to convince your ADHD spouse to go do something together? Then once you're out doing things, your partner says he or she is having "the time of their life."

Guess what? Initiating intimacy is really no different. Offer a little notice, followed by a bit of persistence, and you might find that once your ADHD partner gets engaged in the dance of intimacy, you both end up having a really great time!

~ Sarah A. Ferman, LMFT, MBA, PsyD &
Robert M. Wilford, PhD

Leading ADHD Couples Experts, Dr. Ferman & Dr. Wilford, provide solutions to enhance, rebuild and reconnect ADHD Couples to create loving, joy filled relationships. www.ADHDCouplesSuccess.com

Cooking With ADHD

I attended middle school in the 1960's. That's when the girls took "Home Economics" and learned to cook while the boys took something called "Shop" and learned to use tools and build a bird house.

Our Home Economics class had full-sized, fully equipped kitchens. We worked in groups, were given recipes, and were taught when to do which steps in order to get an entire meal on the table in forty-five minutes, including clean up! At the end of each class, we sat down together and ate whatever we had prepared. Since we had to eat it, we were motivated to make the meal taste good!

Sadly, Home Economics has disappeared from most school curriculums. You might wonder, "Who needs to learn how to cook when there's so much fast food to choose from?" Well, actually, you do!

A few benefits to preparing your own food include knowing what's in it; controlling the fat, salt and sugar content; saving money; and eating healthier meals.

An extra added bonus that may not be so obvious is that cooking involves many aspects of executive functioning. So, when you cook, you're exercising your executive functioning "muscles" and, as a result, helping to manage your ADHD.

Here are a few examples of how cooking at home promotes the practice of executive functioning skills:

Planning: Deciding what you want to cook, finding a recipe, figuring out what you need to buy, and determining when you want to eat—all these use executive functioning skills.

List Making: Writing out the menu and creating a shopping list are crucial. Simply thinking that you'll remember what to buy doesn't always work when your working memory is limited.

Prioritizing: Figuring out what you need to do first is key: you can't mash potatoes until you have boiled them.

Time Management: Cooking requires figuring out how long things take and keeping an eye on time. Trust me, you can't put a 20 pound Thanksgiving turkey in the oven at 1 pm and hope to eat at 3 pm! You have to work backwards to figure out when to start. Also, using a kitchen timer when you cook helps get you in the habit of using timers for everything.

Staying focused: If you lose focus when you're cooking, the results are immediate. You might overcook your food, undercook something, leave out a crucial ingredient or—let's hope this doesn't occur!—burn the house down.

There's something wonderful about a home cooked meal. And it's also wonderful to know that, as you cook that meal yourself, you'll be improving your executive functioning at the same time.

~ Kathy Sussell, ADHD Coach

Kathy Sussell, ADHD Coach, helps teens, college students and adults set goals, manage their time, and get stuff done. Contact her at: www.bravolifecoaching.com (917) 749-9517

"Surround yourself with the dreamers and the doers, the believers and the thinkers, but most of all, surround yourself with those who see the greatness within you, even when you don't see it yourself."

~Edmund Lee

What Do I Love About Where I am Going?

"If you don't change directions, you are going to end up where you are headed." – *Anne Lamott*

Oh, now that's logical. Very. Seems like a sound idea. But, uh, what do I do with that?

ADDers love action. But we often forget what comes from those actions: results. Or a destination . . . . Hang with me for a moment. If you're on the road to Miami, you're going to end up in Miami (probably). The question is: Was Miami the best choice for you? Or did you get talked into it by persuasive friends? Would Orlando have better suited?

Here are three questions to ask yourself each morning (don't worry, they are the same three questions every day!):

1. What road am I on today?
2. What are the most important actions I can take to support movement in that direction?
3. What do I love about where I am going?

~ Catherine Pietrow, Certified ADHD Coach

Catherine Pietrow, Certified ADHD Coach, works with teens to adults to discover their strengths, tap into their best selves and shoot for the stars! www.catherinepietrow.com catherinepietrow@yahoo.com (845) 702-8329

New-fangled or Old-fashioned?

This is the age of technology. We blink . . . and then discover there are new technologies for planning, organizing and remembering. Technology's always tempting, but is it *always* the best choice?

Some people have what I call a "techno" gene. Along with their ADHD brain style, they are innately interested in, and understand, the "new-fangled". Smart phones, apps and technology tools work well for them. I envy them, but I am not one of them.

I am "old-fashioned," the seven-thousand-year history of writing by hand in my genes. Holding a writing implement, putting it to paper, and referring to these notes is a reminder system that works best for me. Star-shaped sticky notes, colored paper and highlighters are interesting and fun enough. A hand-held organizer to track my "to-do"s, appointments and deadlines is new-fangled enough.

"New-fangled" or "old-fashioned": which works best for you?

~Laurie Dupar, PMHNP, RN, PCC

Laurie Dupar is an internationally recognized ADHD expert, coach, author, speaker and fierce advocate for the ADHD community. Connect with her at: www.coachingforadhd.com

Helping Your ADHD Child with Flexible Thinking

It's easy for those with ADHD to get stuck in one way of thinking or reacting to situations. Flexible thinking does not come naturally! So, here's a way to help your child develop it.

Encourage your child to brainstorm a list of 5-7 individuals he or she admires. These could be family members, friends, athletes, artists, singers, teachers, even a treasured pet.

Together, collect pictures of each individual, and add one for your child. Create a collage, putting your child's picture in the middle of the page.

When your child is calm and open-minded, explore how various individuals in the collage might have either similar or different approaches to feeling, thinking and acting.

Following-up by praising your child's ability to identify varied ways of feeling, thinking and acting will give them confidence and skill to solve their own problems.

~ Robin Nordmeyer

Robin Nordmeyer, Strategic Life Coach and ADHD Coaching Specialist helps families get beyond ADHD challenges to experience more success and joy in life ahead. www.livingwellwithadhd.com

Getting Back to Basics

Did you know that our brains cannot function well without plenty of glucose, oxygen, and sleep? Therefore, to live well with ADHD, you should make eating, exercising, and sleeping a priority. When we eat, exercise, and sleep properly, we have more self-control, we make better decisions, we get more done, and we look and feel better too. The extra bonus is that these strategies are free and have no unpleasant side effects. So, get back to basics and start prioritizing good care for yourself. (Having trouble doing that on your own? Get yourself a coach!)

~ Sarah D. Wright

Sarah D. Wright, well-known coach, speaker, and author, specializes in working with adults and college students who want help getting back on track. www.FocusForEffectiveness.com

How Do I "Get" Me?

With experiences as both an Intervention Specialist and, now, an ADHD Coach, I encourage parents to educate their children about their unique brain wiring.

Frustration, confusion, and defiance are often by-products of a child's lack of self-understanding. Having your child embrace an understanding of ADHD is critical in his or her journey towards acceptance of its challenges and related executive function impairments. Your child's age, and, of course, your personal thoughts as a parent, will help determine whether in your discussion you directly use the "ADHD" acronym or, as I often do with younger teens, use a metaphor such as "a cell phone trying to juggle too many open applications at one time". Kids identify easily with that metaphor and the resultant drain on the brain battery! Most importantly, understanding about one's own brain wiring is a vital link in your child's acceptance of the challenges of ADHD, and ultimately in the ability to gain or maintain high self-esteem.

~ Judy A. MacNamee BS, MS, MBA, AAC

Judy A. MacNamee, ADHD Certified Coach, specializes with ages 12 and up, celebrating strengths, reducing obstacles and getting her clients "unstuck!" www.adhdcoachconnect.com
judy@adhdcoachconnect.com (614) 804-6706

To Reach Your Goals, Anticipate the Unexpected

As an ADHD Coach, I often work with professionals who want help in completing a major project or achieving a long-term goal. Typically, they hire me to coach them because they have experienced poor progress and are concerned with not making it to the finish line.

A good example was a client I'll call "Max." At 49 years old, Max was attempting for the third time to get his master's degree through a part-time program.

Although Max was an excellent writer and enjoyed doing academic research, he had a history of failure to complete written assignments. Max hired me so he could finish a major research paper for one of his classes.

Like most people with ADD / ADHD, Max lacked a realistic sense of time about his work. We broke down his studying into small, specific tasks that he could measure. He quickly came to realize that each task he worked on took three-to-four times longer than he had anticipated. So, multiplying his initial time estimate by four made his planning much more realistic.

For Max's research paper, we created a writing schedule with target dates for completing each phase. Meeting the deadline would be tight, but do-able.

However, from the beginning, Max fell behind on actually doing the work as he had planned. Each week, he had a specific reason for what went wrong:

- Laptop died: At a critical juncture, Max's laptop died. Instead of writing that day, he took the laptop in for repair, and learned that would take a week.
- Unable to access a computer: Max knew that some computers were available for graduate student use at his school. But when he showed up, he found that they had all been reserved in advance. Another day wasted.
- Argument with wife: It was critical that Max get to the library by 9:00 a.m. on Saturday in order to get in the necessary hours of research. Instead, he didn't leave the house until noon because, as Max put it: "My wife picked the usual fight when I wanted to leave." It turned out that his wife resented Max being in the graduate program and started arguments about it on a regular basis.

Although seemingly unrelated, these three problems were part of a larger pattern: Max did not have a habit of thinking through what could go wrong nor of taking preventative measures. So, each time something happened, he got derailed. In fact, these "unexpected" roadblocks could actually have been anticipated.

- Laptop repair: Max had been anxious for weeks about his laptop's erratic behavior. He could have taken it in for repair earlier, knowing there was the possibility it could crash at the worst possible time.
- Computer access: As soon as his laptop died, Max could have booked a university computer and made sure he knew the hours it would be available.
- Wife's argument: Considering his wife's history of complaints, Max could have told her in advance that he would be leaving at 8:30 Saturday morning for the library. There was no need for him to stay at home and participate in a chronic argument that went nowhere.

For Max to get his degree, he needed to change his pattern of *reacting* to one in which he began *anticipating*!

Do you have a pattern like Max's? To follow through on your goals, first create a realistic timetable. Then, for each step, ask, "What could go wrong?" and "What can I do about it?"

For an important project, also make sure you have a Plan B.

You'll achieve much more in life once you learn to anticipate the unexpected!

~ Bonnie Mincu, MA, MBA, Senior Certified ADHD Coach

Bonnie Mincu, MA, MBA, is a Senior Certified ADHD Coach and trainer with an international clientele. Drawing upon 23 years corporate experience in executive coaching, training, management and process redesign, Bonnie helps each of her ADHD clients design their own best process and solutions. Since 2001, Bonnie has developed THRIVE with ADD breakthrough tools for procrastination and paralysis, time sense, and planning. Her many step-by-step training programs include online "Procrastination Transformation," "ADHD Productivity Engine," and a Self-Coaching Workbook/CD package. She is an annual presenter at the Virtual ADHD Conference, and teaches her full-day ADHD seminar at NYU. Visit www.thrivewithadd.com

Organized: Who, Me?

Recently someone said to me, "You are so organized!" Amazing! That comment was music to my ears. But, immediately I thought to myself, "If they only knew . . . ."

Am I organized? YES. Is it difficult for me to be organized? YES. So, instead of putting myself down, why not give myself a pat on the back? It is difficult for me to organized, and yet I STILL am organized. Now, that's admirable!

People with ADHD can readily define themselves by the struggle of living with ADHD. Dr. Daniel Amen writes about ANTS (*A*utomatic *N*egative *T*houghts). Just as with ants on a picnic blanket, we want to eliminate negative thoughts. We are people who *have* ADHD, we are not ADHD. Putting ourselves down influences the way we see ourselves and the perception we leave with others.

So, cut yourself some slack. The next time someone compliments you, stand up tall, smile, and say, "Thank you!"

~ Cheryl Gigler, BMed, CCC

Cheryl Gigler is a Certified ADHD Coach and a Certified Educator, empowering adolescents and adults to experience success with ADHD. www.addjoyoflife.com joyoflifecoach@aol.com (260) 415-341

Create New Strategies Using Your Learning Style

Could you unleash your hidden potential by discovering and using your own learning style?

We are all unique human beings, and there are many different ways we learn. Some people are more visual; others learn best by listening; some learn through reading; some have to move to take in information; and still others learn best by doing. Additionally, some people learn best alone while others take in more by interacting in a group.

What happens when you learn in way that is fun, creative, engaging and interesting for you? Likely, you become engaged and fully use your senses. This helps to easily remember things, take them in, be able to reflect back on experiences, and learn for the future.

The world needs different kinds of minds to work together. Find out how your learning style can build your strengths!

~ Chris Bysell Hamrin, PCAC, PCC, ACCG, the first Certified ADHD Coach in Sweden

Chris Bysell Hamrin, the first Certified ADHD Coach in Sweden, specializes in learning styles and creativity when coaching children and young adults. www.Strength2Grow

Are *You* an ADHD Impostor?

In 2001, before Twitter, there was little dialogue about ADHD. When two friends suggested I might "be ADD," I was skeptical. But, I investigated and became a believer.

Today, ADHD is popular and "ADHD Impostors" abound. They laugh, attributing forgetfulness or occasional distraction to "being ADD."

This story is about my life and my success with a *different* type of ADHD Impostor.

Diagnosed at 43, I hired a coach, changed my diet, exercised and took meds. My business was 9 years old and 100% referral. I had more demand than I could handle, and my instincts served me well. When something felt right, I said, "Yes." When it didn't, I said, "Sorry, no." This worked really well right up until the time it didn't.

In 2005, I won a large training contract with an established client. This meant engaging with executives, sourcing instructional content, making financial investments, and delivering training internationally.

That's when my confidence started unraveling. I'd always known I was different. I didn't process information like others, and now I needed to accomplish many new things at once.

This is when the 'impostor' characteristics first described by Dr. Pauline Rose Clance (*The Impostor Phenomenon*) kicked in. I had attributed my success to luck, gargantuan effort, and *not* to ability or competence.

For the record, my contract was renewed *three* times. But I was a wreck. In 2008, I turned 50, my Dad died, two best friendships ended, and work disappeared as the recession slashed budgets. I was menopausal and depressed.

I'd always had trouble facilitating my own thoughts effectively. It seemed I didn't know what I knew. I *did know* in *some* environments. When I was *on*, it was magical. But, when I wasn't, it seemed I just couldn't crack the secret to how I excelled. And I spent too much time alone trying to fix myself and attempting to hide flaws. I never imagined I'd end up embracing these flaws.

The Impostor loves ADHD brains. ADHDers know we're different, feel shame and ruminate more than others. The Imposter's #1 goal is to turn *fears* into *beliefs* so that we avoid hurtful experiences. While protecting us, the Impostor prevents us from accessing our authentic, whole-hearted life.

I let my Impostor run my show for decades and didn't realize a crucial belief for success: *You Can Do This.*

It was when I suspended my most sabotaging beliefs piñata-style and examined them from all sides that I realized what these beliefs actually were and are: *Big Inspiring Possibilities.*

~ Sherri Dettmer Cannon

Sherri Cannon, Executive Coach, ADHD Coach and seasoned workshop leader, has helped individuals and teams around the world thrive by leveraging strengths, collaboration and innovation since 1990. Diagnosed with ADHD in 2001, Sherri specializes in working with multi-function teams, business leaders and innovators of all kinds. As Master Facilitator of Fierce Conversations™ as well as certified StandOut -Strengths™ Facilitator and Coach, Sherri helps professionals leverage their unique strengths and build teams high in trust, innovation, fun and results. For more information, visit www.sherricannon.com

Are You a Helicopter Partner?

Do you hover over your spouse while he/she is doing tasks? Does your nagging, pleading and anger fail to motivate? If so, you may be a helicopter partner!

While helicopter partners are borne from frustration when job after job isn't completed, the problem is that helicoptering doesn't build respect . . . or allow your partner to learn, for him/herself, what works and what doesn't.

So, if this dynamic sounds familiar to you, try these tips:

1. **Remind your partner only once.** Nagging isn't sexy!
2. **Leave it.** Just because you can do it doesn't mean you should.
3. **Don't take responsibility for your partner's actions.**
4. **Let your partner fail.** That's the best way to learn!
5. **Don't do for your partner what your partner can do for him or herself.**

Remember you are building a healthy, equal partner-ship you both can enjoy for years to come.

~Laurie Dupar, PMHNP, RN, PCC

Laurie Dupar is an internationally recognized ADHD coach and thought leader in the ADHD community. Visit her website at: www.CoachingforADHD.com to find more useful strategies.

Planning Ahead for a Successful Semester

It's hard to have a successful semester if you don't know what assignment to do when! So, consider this approach:

1. During the first week of the semester, spend 20-30 minutes each evening with one syllabus, putting due dates for homework, papers, projects and exams into your calendar/planner. Do this for each class.

2. Work backwards from each major due date, entering in your calendar an earlier start date for writing papers or exam review. This will help avoid a last minute crunch.

3. During the first weekend of the semester, take 10-15 minutes to look closely at mid-term and finals weeks in your planner. It's common to have multiple "due dates" or tests around those times. Think ahead, making note in your calendar, about how you might spread out any studying, papers or projects to make those periods more manageable.

Here's to planning ahead for a successful semester!

~ Elizabeth (Liz) Ahmann, ScD, RN, ACC

Liz Ahmann, ADHD coach, works with students and others to identify strengths, pinpoint challenges, clarify goals, develop strategies, and support success. www.lizahmann.com www.lizahmann.blogspot.com

Passion + Action = Success

I coach a terrific teenager, "CK." He's a super active kid, plays sports, and is a real people person. Everyone loves CK. But life gets hard when, because of his ADHD, he can't complete assignments, study for tests, or plan ahead.

He's told me: "I don't study for tests." "I don't do homework." "My mom has given up on me."

But last week something big happened. CK found his passion. He organized teams of kids to collect donations at a coin drop. He raised $5000 in two days. CK then got his school's permission to hire buses to take 100 students to watch their school team play baseball in the state finals. He found a teacher to accompany them as a chaperone. He did all this because he wanted the baseball players to feel the support of their school. He knew he was the one to make it happen. All self-doubt faded away. Now that's passion!

~ *Catherine Pietrow, Certified ADHD Coach*

Catherine Pietrow, Certified ADHD Coach, loves her work with teens through adults to discover their strengths, tap into their best selves, and shoot for the stars, all while keeping a sense of humor!
www.catherinepietrow.com catherinepietrow@yahoo.com
(845)702-8329

My Brother's Journey from Annoying to Inspiring!

My childhood memories of my brother have always been bitter because all I remember was him being punished. I clearly remember how people around us were treating him when we were growing up. My brother was perceived by the majority of the people we knew to be annoying and ill mannered. Because of his hyperactivity, I repeatedly heard the words "stupid' and "reckless" in reference to him.

Fast-forward 30 years, and now my brother is married with 4 beautiful children. He has become one of the most prominent authorities in his community, not only because of his financial success, but mainly because of his caring personality and even-handedness.

It was a beautiful summer day in 2007. It was the big day, the opening of my brother's new industry. I was standing among a crowd of more than 500 guests listening to Governor Brown of California praising my brother. He was speaking about the magnificent idea that my brother had put into action and how proud my brother should feel to be a pioneer in the world for founding the only industry of its kind–an industry that was going to impact both the American economy and the global environment in a positive way!

As I was listening to the Governor, tears ran down my cheeks as I thought back to how, as a child, my brother had been mistreated, misunderstood, bullied and punished almost daily. I reflected on how this change in my brother had taken place.

The change process started when my brother came to the United States as an adult. People around him realized that he was an "out of the box" thinker, had many ideas, and could see the big picture. He started hearing positive comments from various people for the first time in his life. My brother started to feel that, perhaps, he really was smart. He paid attention to that, and his self-esteem started to increase. He was able to compensate for his executive functioning challenges by hiring a good professional executive secretary, and he started working with his strengths and putting his ideas into action.

The more successful my brother became, the more motivated he also became. From the previous endless cycle of bad, worse, and worst, he entered the cycle of good, better, and best! Not only did my brother become an extremely successful entrepreneur, more importantly, he became known for his generosity and for helping many of the disadvantaged people in his community.

It is known that genetic factors play a key role in ADHD. However, the environmental and social factors, I believe, are the ones that can make or break an individual with ADHD. An individual with the "executive functioning" challenges of ADHD can end up in jail or, alternatively, can become highly successful, depending on whether she or he feels broken or whole.

My brother had been living all his childhood, and some years of his adulthood, in an environment that, rather than valuing his gifts, was only paying attention to what he was NOT good at. He lived in a culture that has many great virtues but, unfortunately, can also be punitive, judgmental and full of criticism. When he moved to the United States, my brother was able to absorb all the great virtues from both cultures and combine them together.

Additionally, the experiences he had in the U.S. contributed to a realization that he was indeed a very bright and good person. He started taking advantage of his "out of the box" ways of thinking. Subconsciously, after his move, he started converting all the "negatives" of ADHD into "positives":

- His stubbornness became perseverance, one of the

most important keys to his success.

- His impulsivity transformed into creativity.
- His hyperactivity helped him to travel thousands of miles each month, one of the prerequisites for his success.

I believe that the main reason for any individual's success is high self-esteem, a malleable trait influenced by many socio-cultural factors.

My hope is that by educating the parents, teachers, and other professionals who work with children we will see these bright but misunderstood individuals able to flourish as they should!

~ Roya Kravetz, PCC, BCC, CMC

Roya Kravetz is a Board Certified and ICF Credentialed Life Coach who specializes in strength-based coaching for children, teens, adults, and parents whose lives are affected by ADHD or similar behavioral and/or organizational challenges. Roya is Co-Founder and a Thought-Leader for Parenting 2.0, an international movement that facilitates positive change by nurturing a proactive life skills educational process. She has been published several times and is a regular speaker at local, national and international conferences. Fluent in three languages, Roya coaches clients nationally and internationally. www.adhdsuccesscoaching.com

Couples & ADHD: Counteracting An Emotional Hijacking!

Have you ever been in an argument with your partner and said things you later regret? When we argue, the brain releases cortisol, sounding the fight, flight or freeze alarm. Once it's sounded, the brain loses access to rational thinking and becomes "emotionally hijacked".

Appreciation and gratitude are some of the most effective ways to counteract emotional hijacking. They increase levels of oxytocin, the "tend and befriend" hormone.

To quickly increase oxytocin, try the "Hand Over Your Heart Technique." Simply place your hand over your heart, and concentrate on something you appreciate or are grateful for.

It's difficult to have two opposite emotional experiences at the same time. Finding appreciation will shift your brain state so you regain emotional control and decrease reactivity in the relationship between you and your partner.

~ Sarah A. Ferman, LMFT, MBA, PsyD &
Robert M. Wilford, PhD

Leading ADHD couples' experts, providing solutions that enhance, rebuild & reconnect couples to create loving, joy filled relationships.
www.ADHDCouplesSuccess.com

"Be confident.
Too many days are wasted
comparing ourselves to others
and wishing to be
something we aren't.
Everybody has their own
strengths and weaknesses, and
it is only when you accept
everything you are –
and aren't –
that you will truly succeed.

~Anonymous

Test Myself? You're Kidding!

Who likes taking quizzes and tests? . . . Hmm . . . We are still waiting for some hands to be raised here!

But research shows that testing actually helps you learn! Apparently, the process of recalling information engages the brain fully and helps implant information more firmly. Study tip: Quiz yourself for success!

Here are some sources for questions:

- Study guide from the teacher
- Review questions at the end of a textbook chapter
- Questions you generate from textbook headings, vocabulary, or other parts of your text
- Questions you develop from lecture notes
- Questions posed by fellow students in a study group
- Sample tests or quizzes you find on the internet

The research doesn't say that you have to *like* quizzes or tests . . . only that you may learn best if you take them! So, consider adding self-quizzing to your study skills repertoire!

~ Elizabeth (Liz) Ahmann, ScD, RN, ACC

Liz Ahmann, ADHD coach, works with students and others to identify strengths, pinpoint challenges, clarify goals, develop strategies, and support success. www.lizahmann.com www.lizahmann.blogspot.com

Scheduling Yourself for Success in College

Have you used the website 'ratemyprofessors.com,' or a similar website? These sites are popular because they help college students check out their prospective professors.

In addition to choosing professors whose teaching style matches your particular learning style, you might also pay attention to *when* the classes you sign up for are scheduled.

Consider the following:

- Do you do your best thinking in the morning, afternoon or evening?
- Do you need to exercise before class to prime your brain for learning?
- Do you need time between classes to relax, study, or perhaps finish up last-minute assignments?
- Do you need time to eat something nutritious before any of your classes?

Recognizing what works best for you will help you better thrive in college. When possible, schedule your classes to meet your needs!

~ Roxanne Fouché

Roxanne Fouché, strength-based ADHD coach and consultant, works with – and on behalf of - students and adults with ADHD. Contact her at: Roxanne@FocusForEffectiveness.com (858) 484-4749

Did You Wake up on the "Bad Side" of Your Brain?

You know that saying, "I woke up on the wrong side of the bed"? Sometimes with ADHD we have days when it feels like we have woken up on "the bad side of the brain." On these days, just getting out of bed is an accomplishment, and everything feels overwhelming.

Here's how to make the best out of a "bad brain" day:

- Get up, even if you don't feel like it.
- Continue your daily routines: eat, shower, dress, and take your medication.
- Call in the troops: hang with supportive friends and family.
- Be kind to yourself. Treat yourself to a latte, favorite place, or uplifting movie.
- Ask yourself what might have contributed to your "bad side of the brain" day. Did you sleep poorly? Change your diet? Skip your medication? Are you more stressed? Address the issue if possible.

Use these strategies to minimize the impact of a "bad side of the brain" day, and remember: there's always tomorrow!

~Laurie Dupar, PMHNP, RN, PCC

Laurie Dupar is an internationally recognized ADHD coach and thought leader in the ADHD community. To find more useful strategies, visit her website at: www.CoachingforADHD.com

Design It to Fit Your Life!

Breaking a large task into smaller pieces is a great way to make a project manageable. Recently, I had a college-aged client who was a French major. At the beginning of the semester, he received an assignment to write a 250 word French dictionary, due the last week of the semester–a huge task! He decided he would work on the assignment 3 days per week. We counted the weeks until it was due and did some math. He wrote approximately 10 definitions each of the 3 days he had chosen, and, at the end of the semester he submitted his completed dictionary before the deadline. While his classmates became stressed-out trying to finish the assignment at the last minute, my client was stress free.

Breaking a large task into smaller tasks can be taken a step further by designing the smaller tasks to fit your own lifestyle. Another college-aged client, a music major, was given an assignment to practice his aural scales throughout the semester. This assignment clearly could not be cram-med into a few weeks at the end of the semester. However, evidence of his regular practice would show up in how fluidly he could execute the scales, as well as in the musical 'ear' he would develop. In one coaching session, we took time to brainstorm possible approaches to the task. He attended a college heavily devoted to music, so there were many pianos throughout the campus. My client happened to be a very active, social person and was often walking about campus. I asked how long it would take to practice his scales one time: it was less than 2 minutes! I suggested that every time he walked past a piano on campus, he might practice his scales one time. He thought that plan would be very simple to execute and agreed to the idea. Within 2 weeks, his teacher complimented him, saying that she could tell he was practicing. He was very excited and proud of her compliment, and it served to motivate him even further.

In each of these situations, my client and I were able to create a relatively painless and stress-free method of accomplishing a large task. As a bonus, each of them received an A in class!

~ Jean M. Porto

Jean Porto, certified ADHD Coach and Resilience Coach, specializes in working with high school students, college students and adults wanting to live happier, healthier, more productive lives in partnership with their ADHD challenges. With an advanced certificate in wellness; certification in resilience work; and experience in applying HeartMath tools to ADHD, she supports her clients in creating the lives they have dreamed of. Jean participated as a coach in the seminal 2010 ADHD coaching study linking ADHD coaching to improved executive functioning skills. For more information contact her at jean@inner-inspiration.com or visit www.inner-inspiration.com

Getting off on the Right Foot . . . Or "Goodie Two Shoes"

I'd had a busy day with clients at my home. Grabbing a cup of coffee, I sat down in my recliner. I looked at my feet and noticed something strange. On each foot was a different color shoe! Same style, but different colors! My first response was, "Oh no! I can't believe I did that! Idiot! Who puts on two different color shoes?"

ADHD symptoms follow us across the lifespan, making it difficult to pay attention. Most of us work very hard to get through the day and to not let anyone down. In the grand scheme of things, did wearing two different shoes really matter? Why not give myself credit for a day well lived instead of beating myself up for mismatched shoes? In other words: reframe the negative thinking!

Lesson learned: remember to put your best foot forward . . . whatever color the shoe!

~ Cheryl Gigler, BMed, CCC

Cheryl Gigler is a Certified ADHD Coach and Certified Educator, dedicated to empowering adolescents and adults to experience success with ADHD. www.addjoyoflife.com joyoflifecoach@aol.com (260) 415-3412

Pause to Ponder Positively

Does negative thinking or worry take up too much time in your ADHD thinking? If so, it is time to take back your brain with *positive* thinking.

Positive thinking means approaching life's challenges with a positive outlook. It does not mean avoiding or ignoring the bad things; instead, it involves making the most of potentially bad situations, trying to see the best in other people, and viewing yourself and your abilities in a positive light.

To nurture your positivity try this:

1. Become aware of negative thinking and notice when it happens.
2. Be willing to give equal time to positive thoughts such as what went well, what you learned and what it is possible to do differently.
3. Repeat 1 and 2!

Positive thinking helps you tackle life's challenges by focusing on your strengths and growth, as well as tuning in to effective solutions to problems.

~ Laurie Dupar, PMHNP, RN, PCC

Laurie Dupar is an internationally recognized ADHD coach known for her positive and strength based approach to ADHD. Download her complimentary eBook at www.CoachingforADHD.com

The (Unsustainable) Adventures of Executive Function Mom

I had it ALL together (or at least I thought I did). A professional woman in my mid-thirties, I received awards for things like "tenacity" and "achievement." I was a "get it done" woman. Pitch the ball to me and I'd hit it – every time.

Even going from zero to three kids—in 19 months—didn't (really) faze me. I just put my head down and kept on going! Expanding job, growing family–yep, that was me!

Things were still going well (or so I thought) when my son was diagnosed with ADHD (Inattentive Type) in third grade. I was balancing work, life, home: you know the routine. Sure, I was exhausted at the end of the day, but that was a sign of accomplishment, right? My son's diagnosis explained a lot—including helping me understand other family members who were not (yet) diagnosed—which actually made things a little easier. I kicked into high gear: I researched, advocated, accommodated, and made decisions.

It's Not Sustainable

But there were side effects. The level of conflict in at home had increased, and my ability to perform as a confident leader at work was compromised by the effects of prolonged stress.

Then, my life imploded. I lost my job and, with it, my identity. My relationship with my husband (recovering alcoholic/undiagnosed ADDer) was breaking apart. My confidence was shaken.

When my daughter started having challenges at school—identified by a teacher who knew us well and recognized the signs—I once again pulled it together, re-framing potential futures for all my kids, helping them manage everything from schedules to getting up in the morning to doing homework.

I became EXECUTIVE FUNCTION MOM! After all, if the universe had given me a lovely bunch of "challenged" family members, I should help them ALL, right?! At one point, I even started managing the marketing for my husband's business: why not?

But it didn't (quite) work. My stress levels soared, along with my resentment. I was moody, short-tempered, angry at everyone (including myself). My health suffered both physically and emotionally. I tried to "fix" my life with everything from yoga to anti-depressants. But instead of helping everyone, I was causing more mess than I was cleaning up. Some serious changes needed to be made, and they were for me, NOT my family.

3 Steps to a Self-Care Super-Mom

Over the course of a few years, I relied on a solid spiritual foundation, extreme tenacity, and a whole lot of coaching to reclaim my life. As a result, I have become a *new* kind of super-mom, one who knows that I must make an effort to take care of myself in order to be there for my kids. It took a while to learn that lesson, and there were 3 major steps that got me here.

1. A perspective shift toward compassion. After lots of education and acceptance about the realities of ADHD, I focused on compassion and understanding. It wasn't easy, especially in those moments when I wondered, "Is this his ADD or is he just disrespectful?" When I decided to assume that EVERY unwanted behavior was related to ADD, I accepted that my kids (likely) weren't doing things on purpose. Then, I could problem solve in a way that was supportive rather than judgmental.

2. "Expectations are resentments waiting to happen." The core of my resentment was a long list of expectations that weren't being met. Coaching helped me see that I have a choice to set expectations that are realistic, instead of living in constant frustration. This meant assuming best intentions

(easier said than done), and setting the bar high enough to challenge, but not so high that I set everyone up for failure.

3. Focus on myself. There are several aspects to this. I learned about having compassion for myself (as well as my family), about being willing to let go of resentment, and about not taking everything personally (which is much easier to do when you are the center of your own universe). Self-care also became about actively managing the triggers that put me into stress-mode, and paying attention to daily self-care routines.

If I'm truly honest, I must admit that I still have moments of resentment, and I revert to "Executive Function Mom" more often than I'd like. At the same time, I have found much more enjoyment in life, in my family, and in myself. I realize that a big part of how I experience life lies not in what happens to me, but in how I see and respond to it.

The part of me that wants to control everything loves understanding the importance of perspective, by the way, because it really IS something I can control. If you are a (recovering) Executive Function Mom, I suggest you give it a try–you can control your perspective better than you can control anything else!

~Diane Dempster, MHSA, CPC, ACC

Diane Dempster, MHSA, CPC, ACC is a trainer, speaker, radio show host, Certified Professional Coach, and co-founder of ImpactADHD®. She coaches parents of "complex" kids to radically improve personal and family life, gaining new skills, increasing confidence and learning to use coaching techniques in parenting. Diane received her Master's from the University of Michigan and coaching certification from iPEC. A certified CHADD Parent to Parent teacher, Diane lives in Atlanta with her family. She is committed to living a conscious, balanced and joy-filled life, and helping other parents do the same. For more by Diane, visit her blog on www.ImpactADHD.com

Coaches: We're Teachers Not Tellers!

The greatest enjoyment I get as a coach is when a client I'm working with accomplishes a goal we have set. I feel gratified watching my client get excited about the accomplishment and then look forward to working toward the next goal.

Often what I tell my clients is that it's my job to teach them, not tell them. Tellers work in banks! The job of a coach is to teach you how to develop a solution so you can solve the challenges you are experiencing. To do this, we help clients break the tasks they find challenging into manageable pieces and then approach each piece individually.

I look at the coaching relationship as a partnership. Both my client and I have to be on board, willing and able to keep an open mind. Change doesn't happen overnight: it takes time, but you'll see positive changes if you invest!

~ Sherri B. Silverstein, ADHD Coach and Organizer

Sherri Silverstein of All About Organizing, Inc., is an ADHD Coach and Organizer specializing in adolescents and adults. Contact her at www.organizeyouradhd.org or sherri@organizeyouradhd.org and ask about "The Bucket!"

Tuck Yourself in at Night with a Brain Boosting Blanket!

Do you or your child have a difficult time relaxing to fall asleep at night? A weighted blanket may be just what you need to help you both fall asleep and stay asleep.

Recent studies have shown that deep pressure, the type generated from a weighted blanket, signals the brain to release important neurotransmitters. These brain chemicals, serotonin and oxytocin, naturally calm and relax the body, promoting sleep and, also, stress relief.

Weighted blankets have been tremendously successful helping to promote sleep among children and adults with ADHD, sensory integration disorder, autism spectrum disorder, and restless leg syndrome as well as depression, anxiety, aggression, obsessive-compulsive disorder, post-traumatic stress and bipolar disorder.

Search the term "weighted blanket" on the internet to learn more, including where you can purchase one.

~ Anna Maria Lindell, ADHD Coach and speaker

Anna Maria Lindell, ADD Coach Academy graduate and founder of Advance LP AB, specializes in helping entrepreneurs and other high achievers with ADHD traits to understand their brains, and increase their productivity. www.advancesweden.se

Are You Balanced?

Life balance: would you know it, feel it, recognize it, if you had it?

With ADHD, we can easily focus most of our efforts on just one area of life, such as work or earning money. In the balance, we may neglect other important areas, such as play, fun, or health.

Balance is individual, but this approach can help anyone:

1. Consider the following eight areas of your life and rate how satisfied you are in each on a scale from 1-10, with 10 being very satisfied.

___ Family/friends
___ Career/school
___ Environment (home/work/school)
___ Recreation/fun
___ Personal growth
___ Significant other/partner
___ Money
___ Health

2. Notice the areas you rated low. These are the areas that you might be neglecting, making you feel unbalanced.

3. Identify and take specific actions aimed at increasing your satisfaction in these particular areas.

This will have you well on your way to the balance you desire.

~ *Laurie Dupar, PMHNP, RN, PCC*

Laurie Dupar is an internationally recognized ADHD expert, coach, author, speaker and fierce advocate for the ADHD community. Connect with her at: www.coachingforadhd.com

When Everybody's on the Same Page

Both early intervention and a multi-disciplinary approach in the family and school environments, can be critical in shaping the path of a person with ADHD.

"JJ" is a 10-year-old who has been diagnosed with ADHD, anxiety and depression. He has been raised in a very successful family who has had a difficult time accepting that their child has ADHD and its associated challenges.

JJ's parents had been keeping his diagnosis a secret, even from the school. Not knowing his diagnosis, the school had been giving JJ quite a hard time. JJ's parents received daily complaints about his academic, social and behavior issues. Some of the complaints were about JJ not following directions, not paying attention for long periods of time, not copying questions quickly enough from the board, and lying about doing his homework.

JJ's mom complained that her son was very defiant and out of control. Although both parents claimed that they understood JJ's challenges, their actions didn't show empathy and/or understanding.

Despite the daily struggles with JJ at home, his parents

refused for a long time to ask the school to test JJ and give him accommodations. They felt JJ had to be "perfect" and were extremely worried about destroying that image.

JJ's parents' denial, and the school's resultant lack of information, resulted in JJ both feeling increasingly pressured and hating school even more. Some teachers, such as the math teacher, took points away from him because he solved all the math problems in his head and did not write down the steps. Also JJ got an "F" on a test for organizational skills since he has difficulty with the school's organizational system. He has also often been confused about his homework because the teacher sometimes writes it on the board and sometimes posts it on the website.

A lack of understanding of JJ's challenges also hindered JJ in building supportive relationships with his teachers. One day, JJ stopped talking in class because he was upset and didn't want to cry in front of his classmates. The teacher, however, thought JJ was just being difficult, and she punished him for his silence. Because JJ is a very bright child, teachers have often thought he was being manipulative when he was actually feeling shy and scared.

When JJ's parents realized how his problems were affecting his grades, they knew something had to be done, and they came to me for coaching. Through coaching, JJ's parents educated themselves about ADHD and started to understand their son's challenges. They were very impressed by the insight JJ showed during our sessions. Over time, they became convinced that they should ask the school for a meeting. We worked on the issues they were going to discuss during the meeting, and we planned for JJ to lead the meeting, addressing the things he wanted to change. Eventually, both his parents and the school started building upon JJ's strengths and talents, which were numerous.

Once his parents started listening to and advocating for him, JJ's transformation was amazing. JJ even smiles and laughs in coaching sessions now! He is a leader and has started advocating for himself in school as well.

~ Roya Kravetz, PCC, BCC, CMC

Roya Kravetz is an ICF Credentialed Life Coach who specializes in strength-based coaching for children, teens, adults, & parents whose lives are affected by ADHD or similar behavioral and/or organizational challenges. Roya is Co-Founder and Thought-Leader for Parenting 2.0, an international movement that facilitates positive change by nurturing a proactive life skills educational process. She is an author speaker and is fluent in three languages, Roya coaches clients nationally and internationally. www.adhdsuccesscoaching.com

Create a Positive Story about ADHD

From picture books to cartoons, children are taught storytelling from a young age. Storytelling is an integral part of their self-development. In fact, it's common for children to identify themselves as the main character in their own stories, and include details from their family lives. Strong research indicates a child's sense of well-being and security is affected by how parents relate their own stories to them. Particularly for children with ADHD, it is imperative that parents foster a positive mindset and frame the ADHD in an optimistic story.

Write a fun story with your kids about a character who has ADHD. List all his/her empowering traits. Draw cartoons that emphasize positive ADHD qualities like enthusiasm, passion, and creativity. This will help children adopt a positive story about their own ADHD, giving them a sense of pride and confidence.

~ Dr. Billi Bittan, MA, PhD, ADHD Specialist, NeuroCognitive Behavioral Therapist and Coach

Dr. Billi, PhD, ADHD Specialist, Neuro-Cognitive Behavioral/Expressive Arts Therapist/Coach. Reframe Your Narrative, Change Your Life, Leverage ADHD to Your ADDvantage. www.AttentionB.com DrBilli@AttentionB.com (855) Dr-Billi

Create an Action Board!

An "action board" is a tool that can help you focus on what is important to you, identify goals, and get clarity on the action steps that lead to follow through!

An action board is like a vision board: you collect pictures, words, quotations, and other items that catch your eye or inspire you. NO SHOULDS! If a picture grabs your attention, looks or feels right, tear it out! If you have any goals in mind, grab pictures of action steps as well. Then paste your collection onto a big piece of paper and look at what goal or goals the board inspires you toward. Finally, title it, identify steps, and consider target dates toward your goal(s).

In the process of creating an action board, we spend time considering our goal(s), finding the right pictures, and putting them together. We literally *see*: "This is important" and "This is how to achieve it." This clarity and motivation can propel us to action!

~Laurie Dupar, PMHNP, RN, PCC

Laurie Dupar is an internationally recognized ADHD coach and thought leader in the ADHD community. To find more useful strategies, visit her website at: www.CoachingforADHD.com .

"We can complain because rose bushes have thorns or rejoice because thorn bushes have roses."

~Abraham Lincoln

Couples & ADHD: Avoiding a Sea Of Negativity

You absolutely can make real changes in your ADHD-impacted relationship. Change just a few small habits together to increase closeness and avoid a sea of negativity.

Here are 4 simple steps that you and your partner can adopt to shift the dynamics today:

1. Focus first on what *is* working instead of always focusing on what's not.
2. Adopt positive habits: say "please" and "thank you" often, and mean it.
3. Communicate clearly and politely with each other. Convert demands into requests. Take an extra minute to use a heartfelt voice, and try looking into your partners' eyes.
4. Before agreeing to do anything, make sure you can actually do it. Saying "yes" to your partner means that you are making a promise. It's better to tell your partner up front that the request may not be possible than to cause disappointment with inaction later.

~ Sarah A. Ferman, LMFT, MBA, PsyD &
Robert M. Wilford, PhD

Leading ADHD couples experts, Dr. Ferman & Dr. Wilford, provide solutions to enhance, rebuild and reconnect ADHD couples to create loving, joy filled relationships. www.ADHDCouplesSuccess.com

Laying Down the Tracks

Research about memory and learning, otherwise known as "laying down the tracks," shows that we remember:

- 10% of what we read
- 20% of what we hear
- 30% of what we see
- 50% of what we hear and see together
- 70% of what we say and think
- 90% of what we do/teach

What's going on between 10% and 90% retention? An increasing amount of action and involvement with the information!

In medical school instructors reach for 90% retention and mastery with their adage, "see one, do one, teach one." Teach the concept – it's the ultimate brain boost!

How do you shoot for the 90%? Try these ideas:

- Explain the concept or topic to someone else.
- "Teach" the information in front of a mirror.
- Create a voice memo going over the topic.
- Visualize the concept with all its moving parts.
- Get your body moving!

~ Catherine Pietrow, Certified ADHD Coach

Catherine Pietrow, Certified ADHD Coach, works with teens and adults to discover their strengths, tap into their best selves, and shoot for the stars. catherinepietrow@yahoo.com (845) 702-8329

Dreams Do Come True!

"Johnny," like so many college freshmen with ADHD, was bright, charming and enthusiastic, but also immature, disorganized, and naïve. He'd been quite successful in high school, which had helped get him into the prestigious private college he was now attending, and he had gone off to college determined to make it on his own terms. Not unexpectedly, he was unaware of how the structure and accountability of high school and home—the very things he had chafed against—had been important to his previous success. His great dream was to become a doctor, but by the time I met him at the beginning of his sophomore year, he was on academic probation.

Johnny, like many bright students, had managed to get by on intelligence. But college demanded more from him, and his old strategies—such as they were—weren't working for him. I coached him for five months, helping him to become aware of his strengths and challenges and to develop the systems and skills he needed to get back on track and stay there. After one term, Johnny's grades improved enough that he was off academic probation. He was doing so well we decided to terminate the coaching.

Four years later, I heard from Johnny again. He was now in a very demanding one-year master's program in which he had enrolled to increase his odds of getting into med school, and he needed my help.

This time we worked together for four months. Johnny had matured a lot in the intervening years, and his ability to use the coaching and apply himself was extraordinary. He worked harder than he'd ever worked before, and it paid off. He graduated first in his class, and gave a brilliant valedictorian speech! Then he was off for a summer internship at a medical research lab while he waited to hear from the med schools he'd applied to.

Six months later, I got one of the most wonderful emails I have ever received:

> *Hi Sarah,*
>
> *I hope you are doing well. I certainly am, since I start med school next month!! Thank you for all the guidance and advice in the past. There is no doubt in my mind I could not have got to this point without your coaching. I DID IT!!!!*
>
> *— Johnny D., fMD (future MD)*

I have rarely been so happy for anyone. Coaching really can make dreams come true!

~ Sarah D. Wright

Sarah D. Wright is a well-known ADHD coach, speaker, and author. She has been a scientist, engineer, corporate executive, and entrepreneur, but her true calling is coaching. Coaching people affected by ADHD for well over a decade, Sarah is the author of *ADHD Coaching Matters: The Definitive Guide*, co-author of *Fidget to Focus*, and contributing author to the best-selling *365 Ways to Succeed with ADHD* series. She helped establish both the ADHD Coaches Organization and the coaching and consulting company, Focus For Effectiveness, LLC. She specializes in working with adults and college students who want help getting back on track. Contact her at Sarah@FocusForEffectiveness.com

Time Outs are Not Just for Toddlers

In our family of four children, two with ADHD, emotional impulsivity ran high, as it does for many with ADHD. Playfulness could quickly turn to overwhelm and then to anger—not just for my kids, but for me as well.

One day my 8 year old took friends on a tour of our new home. Passing the laundry room, he explained, "This is where Mom takes her time-outs." For clarification, his friends asked, "This is where you take your time-outs?" "No", he replied, "this is where *Mom* takes her time-outs."

It's true. The laundry room was a sanctuary for me when things got overwhelming and I wanted to avoid getting out of control. Behind the closed door I would breathe deeply until my emotions settled.

When your emotions threaten to erupt, give yourself permission to take a time-out, get back in control, and be the sane adult and parent your children need.

~Laurie Dupar, PMHNP, RN, PCC

Laurie Dupar is an internationally recognized ADHD coach and thought leader in the ADHD community. Visit her website to find more useful strategies: www.CoachingforADHD.com .

Begin Again

What does it mean to begin again? How do you do it?

Whenever you feel you're stuck, try asking yourself, "What have I stopped doing that supported me and made me feel empowered and positive?" You might have stopped taking your vitamins or medication, for example. Perhaps you stopped attending a support group, working out, or using your planner. The trick is to notice sooner rather than later, and then simply pick up where you left off. Although it's easy to beat yourself up for forgetting, and slipping back into old habits, being judgmental just tends to keep you stuck.

Start over with love and compassion for yourself. Try visualizing someone you love and trust gently taking you by the hand, saying, "Come, let's begin again." Then picture yourself placing one foot in front of the other, taking that first step forward. It may be a baby step, but it will be a step in the right direction.

~ Kathy Sussell, ADHD Coach

Kathy Sussell, ADHD Coach, helps teens, college students and adults set goals, manage their time, and get stuff done. Contact her at: www.bravolifecoaching.com (917) 749-9517

From Fun to Forever

The gift of ADHD can make your relationship fun early on. One day, you're cooking *chicken piccata* for the first time; the next day, you're taking salsa dance lessons. But later, after the kids, and the mortgage, and twenty-five years together, "spontaneity"" can start to look like "irresponsibility" and forgetting an anniversary can look like "She doesn't love me anymore." So, once your ADHD is diagnosed, here are some tips that will help:

1. Know these behaviors have a *biological* basis.
2. Make sure your medication is optimized.
3. Make a list of things you *like* and *value* about each other. Look at it regularly.
4. Watch for entrenched behavior patterns. They will take time to identify and change.
5. Remember you are in this together. Don't wait for one partner to "get better."
6. Cultivate fun and romance.

Remember: the love and commitment aren't gone, they just aren't always visible.

~ Mike Fedel

Mike Fedel leads performance-and-discussion groups focusing on adult ADHD and relationships. His primary interest is in public outreach and education. Reach Mike at:
www.mikesscratchpadd.wordpress.com mfedela2@gmail.com

Long Term Effects of NOT Taking ADHD Medication

When deciding to use medication as a management strategy for ADHD symptoms, considering the long term consequences and risks is important. It's common to contemplate and weigh the long term risks of taking ADHD medication on the developing mind and body.

But, what about the long term consequences and risks of NOT taking ADHD medication?

- Increased risk of becoming addicted to other substances later in life
- Increased risk of getting divorced
- Increased trouble finding and keeping a job
- Increased risk of low self esteem
- Increased chance of doing poorly in school
- Increased risk of poor social relationships
- Increased risk of car accidents
- Increased chance of having trouble with the law

Taking or not taking ADHD medication is a personal decision. So, consider all sides to make the best choice(s).

~Laurie Dupar, PMHNP, RN, PCC

Laurie Dupar is an internationally recognized ADHD expert, coach, author, speaker and fierce advocate for the ADHD community. Connect with her at: www.coachingforadhd.com

My Journey from ADHD to PhD

I didn't know it then, but my journey with ADHD began when I was a child. As a rambunctious young girl, it was difficult to sit still in school. I was scolded often: pay attention, stop talking, quit fidgeting! Though I put hours into my studies, my parents never felt my grades reflected my true intellectual capabilities. Soon, I stopped trying so hard, except for gym class and sports where I was able to easily shine.

Socially, I was the odd one out. My teachers expected me to be more like the other kids, and my peers teased me for being a tomboy and liking sports. At one point, I was cast in the school play as a billy goat because my teacher thought the role fit my hyperactive personality; plus, my name is Billi. It was humiliating.

Life turned around when I started gymnastics as a teenager. In the gym, I discovered something that interested me and suited my energetic personality. At last, I had an outlet to be creative and active! Because of my passion, I was able to discipline myself and excel, winning awards and receiving praise and recognition from both coaches and peers.

Slowly, I began to shift my perspective when I realized how my hyperactivity, creativity and out-of-the-box thinking could be assets: how I could succeed because of these very traits that others saw as impairments. I went on to college and studied physical education, choosing this major because it was the perfect avenue in which to channel my high energy. I graduated with honors.

Afterwards, I opened a wellness center where I taught women how to improve body image holistically through nutrition and exercise. Being in a profession that incorporated physical activity suited me. Later, I developed curricula for elementary students utilizing movement and play. I knew from experience that there was a void in the system, a void that alienated kids who focus and process information better through fidgeting or physically moving.

Following that, I got my master's degree in expressive arts therapy and eventually my Ph.D. in education. Initially, my peers criticized me for pursuing a multi-disciplinary approach, calling it "unfocused." The university didn't know where to place me. But I knew that honing in on what interested me, even if it didn't follow academic norms, would motivate me.

Around this time (mid-40s) is when I was diagnosed with

ADHD. I took my daughter for an evaluation, and, while in the office, the psychologist asked, "What about you, young lady?" Given the many roles I had juggled successfully, I was shocked at the suggestion. But I thought back to my childhood and realized how my behaviors seemed to mirror my daughter's—trouble focusing, difficulty completing uninteresting tasks, and not achieving full potential in school. I decided that if I expected my daughter to be tested, I should too.

The results revealed that I had ADHD with an extremely hyperactive component. With the diagnosis, I reflected on my life and saw how the ADHD diagnosis made sense. I was always participating in many sports, always on the go, and literally running from place to place. I was also shifting from one professional realm to the other throughout the day, not sticking with any one task for too long.

I realized I had unknowingly developed coping strategies to compensate for my ADHD. I purposely kept myself physically and mentally busy, as that's what naturally stimulated the chemicals in my brain and kept me motivated. Essentially, I was self-medicating (raising nor-epinephrine and dopamine) to stay interested, focused, and avoid boredom by keeping myself constantly moving.

Once diagnosed, I educated myself and realized I wanted to educate others. I designed my career to include creativity and kinesthetic movement. As a result, I transformed my hyperactivity into an asset for my career: my high energy works for me in the fields of physical education, coaching and expressive arts therapy. My creativity became an asset when I successfully connected expressive arts therapy with my education/pedagogy background. By going with my natural talents/interests and strengthening my strengths, I have a successful career not in spite of my ADHD, but because of it.

I like to use the words "traits" or "assets" instead of "impairments" or "deficits" because I believe ADHD traits can be leveraged into assets to work in your favor. Why dwell on the negative? If you have it, you have it. You might as well learn to love parts of it and deal wisely with the rest of it.

Focusing on my personal strengths, and leveraging my unique ADHD traits to my ADDvantage, were, and still are, my key to success and happiness. This is the positive side of ADHD that I choose to embrace. It's what my Leverage ADHD system™ is all about. I hope you will choose it for yourself, too.

~ Dr. Billi Bittan, MA, PhD, ADHD Specialist, NeuroCognitive Behavioral Specialist and Coach

Dr. Billi Bittan, MA, PhD, ADHD Specialist, Neuro-Cognitive Behavioral/Expressive Arts Therapist and Coach, developed the Leverage ADHD System™ to empower others to transform ADHD challenges into assets. She's the author of *Be the Chief Executive of Your Executive Functions* and co-authored *Mastering the Art of Success* with Jack Canfield, *Roadmap to Success* with Deepak Chopra, and the bestselling ADHD Awareness books. Speaking appearances include conferences, webinars and events for ACO, ADDA, CHADD, Succeed with ADHD Telesummit, Expressive Therapies Summit and Vibrant Brain Summit. Her passion is helping you reframe your narrative, change your life and Leverage ADHD to Your ADDvantage.
www.AttentionB.com DrBilli@AttentionB.com (855) DR-BILLI

Be "Your Own Best Thing": Embrace Your Own Best Self!

In Tony Morrison's book *Beloved*, the character Sethe is told, "YOU [are] your own best thing." Yet, for individuals with ADHD, self-appreciation is easily pushed aside.

As Sethe was told, remember to embrace the best things about you: your talents, your gifts, your heart, your self. Give yourself the focus, compassion and forgiveness that you give others in your life. Not only will you experience a shift in balance, but also you'll also be giving yourself the gifts of self-acceptance, self-love and room for growth which, themselves, are also stress-relieving and healing.

Along with other important ADHD practices (meditation, exercise and healthy diet) practice embracing your own best, awesome self, talents, imperfections and all, EVERY-DAY. "How?" you wonder. Take the time to find your own best way. Create, embrace and celebrate your own best self!

~ Melissa Fahrney, MA, ACC, CSS

Melissa Fahrney, certified ADHD, Career Development & Heart-based Stress Management Coach for Youth/ADDults BRAIN STRATEGIES + HEART IQ = STRESS FREE SUCCESS www.addheartworks.com

How to Prioritize a Long To-Do List

We ADDers are infamous for at least two things: inability to prioritize and (in part as a result) looooong to-do lists. A difficult combination!

There are many ways to structure your "to-do"s to prioritize. Here's one:

- Ask yourself, simply, "If I could do only TWO things today, what would they be?"

If even this simple method defies the ability of an overwhelmed mind to narrow things down to the most relevant, here's another approach:

- A friend who's a successful retired entrepreneur calls her approach "3 Minutes. 3 Hours. 3 Days." If you were to write this at the top of your to-do list and keep it there, you could use it to structure your priorities based on what needs attending to *now, soon,* and *later.*

Make one of these approaches to your list a habit, and your long to-do list will get shorter by the day.

~ *Alan Brown, creator of* ADD Crusher™

Alan Brown, entrepreneur and ADHD coach, created ADD Crusher™ videos and tools that help ADHD teens/adults live to their potential. Reach him at www.ADDCrusher.com

"Imagine we each come onto this earth with a crayon box...
Now, you may get the eight pack, or the sixteen pack, but it's all in what you do with the crayons, the colors that you're given.
Don't worry about drawing within the lines or coloring outside the lines.
Color outside the lines. Color right off the page!"

~ Unknown

Wisdom of a Mom's Inner Voice

I sat in the doctor's office trying to fight back the tears, pleading with him to give us other options . . . nothing. I didn't completely trust the doctor. But, what else was there? I was a parent. I didn't know what to do. It felt as if I were supposed to know, but I didn't, which was very scary.

My oldest daughter was diagnosed with ADHD, inattentive type. This explained her shyness and daydreaming. She was 10 years old, with extremely low self-esteem and high anxiety. Lost, with no one to talk to, no resources, I did what I believed at the time to be unthinkable. I gave her medication. For six years, frustration and fear crowded my thoughts during the trial and error of finding the right medication and dosage. It felt like a cold science experiment with my daughter as the guinea pig.

Finally: progress. She was doing better in school. Her self-esteem was improving. Yet, her success on medication wasn't enough. I kept hearing questions I couldn't quiet in my head: What if these pills had long term negative effects? What if all the studies are wrong and I'm risking my daughter's health, her future? I had no answers.

As the years passed, my daughter became even more

withdrawn from friends and family. She was thin with little or no appetite. I gave her melatonin to fight the insomnia, a side effect of her medication. How was she supposed to focus in school when she was exhausted from not sleeping at night? All my fears about medication were staring me right in the face. Now what?

Freshman year of high school came. Anxiety was stifling her. She hyper-focused on getting good grades. Yet, perfectionism as a goal left her feeling like a failure at every turn. Every "A" earned was only relief, never a celebration. She immediately saw the next challenge ahead only to embrace it with even higher expectations. Sleep continued to be a problem. Maybe she slept 4-5 hours a night. I became her tutor, her study-buddy. It was exhausting. Countless hours of studying night after night with her taught me something: her anxiety was spiraling out of control.

I started really listening to the questions in my mind. Was my daughter dependent on her medication? Not addicted, but mentally dependent? Was she trapped by the false belief the pills were what made her smart? I searched for other treatments. Then, I waited for a sign. A sign to tell me she might be ready for a change.

Early in her sophomore year, my daughter hesitantly told me

she needed a dosage increase. "Is that what you want to do?" I asked. Through tears she cried, "I hate taking the pills." I struggled with her tears and her words as she described herself feeling emotionally flat, in a fog. This was the turning point I had been waiting for. I introduced her to "brain-training."

I had heard many criticisms of this type of program: the cost, the time. But I didn't care. Sitting with someone and "playing brain-games" couldn't hurt I thought. In my mind, it was less risky than experimenting with more medication. The fact is, for me, no study was enough to convince me with 100% certainty whether any treatment was going to work for my daughter.

The intense, one-on-one, brain training program, 3-4 times a week for 9 months resulted in huge gains in all my daughter's cognitive skills. Her focus and processing speed after brain-training and *without* medication measured well above what it had been before brain training, on medication. The training changed her brain and, in fact, her whole life!

We no longer view my daughter's ADHD as something to be treated. As a family, we embrace a healthy brain lifestyle for each of us through exercise, diet and meditation. I'm now aware of what we, as parents, don't talk about amongst each other: ADHD and how to manage it.

I now know that what helps ease one person's symptoms may not help someone else's. Medication is one of many options to consider in boosting brain function. I no longer hold any firm beliefs about medication, other than that it had a time and place for my daughter. It served its purpose.

What I *have* learned is to trust myself. I now listen to those internal questions: they're talking to me for a reason.

I have also learned that my daughter is not broken or damaged. She's an artist with an especially tender heart towards children. She's sensitive, smart, wacky, and funny. She isn't limited by ADHD. Instead, acknowledging her ADHD allowed her to embrace who she is, and to build her future her own way.

Parenting is challenging in any circumstance. Parenting a child with ADHD is even harder. Still, I wouldn't trade a minute of it for anything. My daughter is the most amazing and gifted person I've ever met. And I'm not just saying that because I'm her Mom!

~ Carlene Bauwens, ADHD Coach

Carlene Bauwens, Certified Mental Health First Aid Responder and ADHD Coach at About-FACE Life Coaching, supports parents in understanding how their child's ADHD brain works. Through individual and group coaching, strategies are developed to reduce chaos and create calm for the entire family. Carlene partners with high school and college students transitioning to young adulthood, incorporating time management and organization strategies to provide support as they move into greater freedom and independence. Carlene supports ADHD awareness through her blog at http://eyeoncompassion.com. Coaching is offered in-person, via telephone and on-line. For more information, contact Carlene at eyeoncompassion@att.net or visit www.coachcarlene.com

What is Your Rainbow Playlist?

I learned about a "Rainbow List" from one of my mentors, David Giwerc, owner and director of the ADD Coach Academy. We can make a rainbow list by reflecting on, and writing down, great moments or days in our lives. It is the kind of list that helps us remember our successes rather than our failures. It also helps us remember what is important to us and what we are good at or proud of in our life. The rainbow list is a list we can turn to when we are having a bad day or feeling extra doubtful. We can use it to look back at, review, and be reminded of our successes and strengths.

A fun twist on the "Rainbow List" is to create a "Rainbow Playlist" of your favorite or most meaningful songs: a collection of music that will remind you of your strengths and encouraged and uplift you.

What would you want on your "Rainbow Playlist"?

~Laurie Dupar, PMHNP, RN, PCC

Laurie Dupar is an internationally recognized ADHD coach and thought leader in the ADHD community. To find more useful tips, visit her website at: www.CoachingforADHD.com .

The Big Apple

Recently I traveled to New York City for a funeral. Afterwards we went to a family member's house for a meal. A large group of us sat in a circle talking and one young man said, "I heard that you are a Life Coach. What made you go into that field?" I straightened up, smiled, and said, "I became a Life Coach after I was diagnosed with ADHD."

There was a collective gasp in the room! "No, not you, but you are so smart!" they protested. I looked at these savvy New Yorkers dressed in black, and said, "ADHD is not an intelligence deficit: it is a performance deficit."

Some years earlier, I wouldn't have been forthcoming about my own ADHD. Oddly enough, through an ADHD diagnosis, I found my true voice. A voice I used that day in the Big Apple.

~ Cheryl Gigler, BMed, CCC

Cheryl Gigler is a Certified ADHD Coach and Certified Educator, dedicated to empowering adolescents and adults to experience success with ADHD. www.addjoyoflife.com joyoflifecoach@aol.com (260) 415-3412

How to Fix What's Wrong (in Your Relationships)

When dealing with conflict in your relationships, do you find yourself fixated on being right?

We often see our own view of a situation as the ONLY interpretation of a specific story. Yet, problems lurk around the corner when these black or white (me or you) interpretations begin to develop lives of their own. When this happens, ADDers, especially, can start to spin around endlessly in our minds, developing story monsters with long, growing tails. What soon follows is feeling frustrated, alone, confused, hurt, small and overwhelmed, while desperately trying to pretend to look strong and confident. Ultimately, this energy-draining struggle may cause us to want to give up on ourselves or our important relationships.

Consider: What might be possible if you choose, even just once, to let your defenses down and look at the "conflict" at hand as if "nothing is wrong here"?

~ *Sanlia Marais, PACC, Consciousness Coaching®*

Sanlia Marais, Professional ADHD/Consciousness Coach, loves supporting adults, teens and parents to celebrate their relationships by befriending their emotions and innate strengths. Contact her at: sanlia@entreecreativechange.com www.entreecreativechange.com

Remember Your 'Three Blessings' Every Day

It's easy to start feeling down during a school semester. Not understanding a topic, getting a bad grade–it can all feel overwhelming very quickly. While life does have its ups and downs, when we are down, we often forget to notice the positive things that are happening and, instead, we get stuck seeing only the negative. What we notice becomes our reality.

Martin Seligman, the creator of Positive Psychology, has done an extensive amount of research on happiness and provides an extremely simple solution to combat feeling down. It's called 'Three Blessings.' Every day, take 10 minutes to write down three things that went well that day and why each went well. These can be huge events but they don't have to be. They may be as simple as having had your favorite ice cream for dessert. The difference this simple practice can make in your life is amazing!

~ Jean M. Porto

Jean Porto is a certified ADHD Coach and Resilience Coach, specializing in high school students, college students and adults. See more at: www.inner-inspiration.com

I Feel Different

It was not a big jump for me from coaching about international etiquette and protocol to coaching about brain diversity.

Let's start with international etiquette. I had a client new to the culture of the U.S. Her English was very good, but she had a noticeable accent that prompted others to immediately ask, "So, where are you from?" Unfortunately, what most would consider a friendly ice-breaker made her feel worlds apart from others.

Her look, accent, and even her typical metaphors caused her to feel different. She tried acting like others in an effort to fit in at work and social events. This "acting" caused her great stress, due to repressing who she really was, and actually had the opposite effect from what she had intended. Instead of helping my client make more friends, her efforts to fit in often caused her to be perceived as insecure and arrogant.

Shift to neurodiversity. "I have always known I am different." Can you relate to this statement? Many with ADHD can. ADHD brain traits are noticeable in the ways we behave and the ways we process information. We tend to be in our heads more than in our bodies. Multiple ideas are often bursting to be expressed, and a lack of self-regulation can cause others to perceive us as impulsive, impatient, and sometimes even rude.

During high school, we desperately want to blend in, and we desperately want to stand out. For those of us with ADHD these contradictory emotions often remain well into adulthood. Why is it so hard for us to "graduate" from high school emotions even after we've received our diplomas? Even when we feel different as adults, we sometimes think first impressions are a matter of life and death because we believe they can make or break our standing in the community. The consequence is that we are always feeling that we are not enough, so we hide who we are.

Aren't we all tired of pretending? Consider this: meeting someone who is as comfortable with their flaws as they are with their strengths is very attractive.

So, I supported my client (new to the U.S). by challenging her to experiment with being her authentic self in public for a week and to record how she felt and how she was accepted.

She could not wait for the next session to report back. During the week, my client had worn a red dress, purple shoes, and a flower in her hair—not literally, but she really had flaunted her true self. She did not wait to be approached; instead, she initiated conversations with others. She decided to feel flattered when they asked about her country of origin. She spent the week expressing all that she is—smart, loud, and charming, and she held court all night long.

Our brain diversity often makes those of us with ADHD feel like we are from another culture, sometimes even another planet! We commonly feel we don't belong and often feel on the outside of most circles. However, the truth is that we have a different, not better or worse, way of relating to the world.

Although we sometimes get distracted, we also have great drive, determination and hyper-focus once our attention is engaged. We may not always say what's appropriate, but we are often funny and can be great conversationalists. We won't always be in line with what everyone else is thinking, but we have great ingenuity, spontaneity and creativity to bring to a conversation, work project or relationship.

It has been said that each individual's greatest desire is to contribute. When we fully understand that each of us has a piece of humanity's puzzle, we can begin to understand that what makes us different—or unique, to use a more positive word—is what makes us infinitely valuable.

~ Angelis Iglesias, ADHD ASD Coach

Angelis Iglesias, ADHD ASD Coach, focuses on multi-cultural and multi-generational coaching. Originally from Puerto Rico, Angelis has worked as a cross-cultural communications consultant and now uses her background to help coach individuals, couples and families. She is both a mother and grandmother of kids with ADHD mind traits. She has seen first-hand how ADHD affects the entire family and believes in coaching the family as a unit. Angelis also believes in creating a safe space where clients pursue their desired outcomes in the areas of work, relationships, and quality of life. For more information, visit mindheartcoach.org

Solving Hour-Long Showers

What can they possibly do in there for an hour??? And when they emerge some sixty minutes later, with hair still dry and footprints that indicate very little soap was ever used–what's happening?

Think of the bathroom as a time warp! Once in, time ceases to exist . . . especially if you have ADHD. Bathrooms are the last places in the house most of us consider putting a clock or timer. Yet, without those, how do they know when to emerge from the shower? When the water gets cold, of course!

The solution is simple: stock the bathroom with as many timing devices as you can. Shower clocks for that wash, rinse and repeat cycle. A two-minute liquid timer to make sure teeth are brushed just long enough.

And finally, the **pièce de résistance?** A wall clock, preferably analog, that can be seen from any bathroom position.

~Laurie Dupar, PMHNP, RN, PCC

Laurie Dupar is an internationally recognized ADHD expert, coach, author, speaker and fierce advocate for the ADHD community. Connect with her at www.coachingforadhd.com

Couples & ADHD: Manifesting What You Want

Whatever we focus our thoughts on, or pay more attention to, seems to increase. Have you ever set your eye on a particular make and model of a car you're wishing to buy? Almost overnight, you start seeing more and more of that exact car everywhere you look.

While a massive spike in car sales is possible, what's more likely is that when you focus your attention on a specific make and model, your brain actually notices more of that type of car driving around you.

The same is true in relationships. If you focus on what's NOT working, the broken stuff becomes all you see. The converse is true as well: keeping your eye on what IS working is a powerful tool to outsmart your brain, notice the positive, and manifest all that's good in your relationship.

~ Sarah A. Ferman, LMFT, MBA, PsyD &
Robert M. Wilford, PhD

Leading ADHD couples experts, Dr. Ferman & Dr. Wilford, provide solutions to enhance, rebuild and reconnect ADHD couples to create loving, joy filled relationships. www.ADHDCouplesSuccess.com

Math + ADHD = Correct Answer

As a parent in our local school district, I have helped on several teacher hiring committees. Last Friday I watched, for the third day in a row, a teaching demo of the Pythagorean Theorem for the right triangle.

I had a mind-wandering ADD moment—often when my best ideas happen. And it clicked: it's all about the relationship! Math, chemistry, life, people, motivation, anxiety, strengths, attention. It's been under my nose, but I was too anxious in math class to have ever seen it.

I started playing with math equations. I don't love math, but I love relationships. Here are a few. I invite you to create some of your own.

Doubt decreases, Motivation increases

Anxiety decreases, Insight increases

Exercise + Time Alone = Clear Direction

Interest + Correct Learning Style = Focus

Clear Intention + Mindfulness = Better Working Memory

~ Catherine Pietrow, Certified ADHD Coach

Catherine Pietrow is a Certified ADHD Coach helping teens and adults find their strengths, keep their sense of humor, and negotiate life on their ADHD terms! www.catherinepietrow.com (845) 702-8329 catherinepietrow@yahoo.com

Bridging the Great Divide Between Ideas and Action

One of my passions is coaching people with ADHD who know they want to experience more satisfaction and success in their lives but are unsure as to what actions will best support this. I love being able to help them discover new ways of managing their ADHD and creating new strategies that maximize their strengths and minimize their challenges.

Throughout the years, I have discovered that a large number of entrepreneurs struggle with ADHD. These adults are gifted with a zillion great business ideas, but they often get stuck because they are not sure how to put those ideas into action. Whether you are an ADHD entrepreneur or not, it's not a lack of ideas that prevents you from enjoying success and productivity, it is closing the gap, bridging the divide, between your ideas, and the necessary follow-through with actions that make things happen.

Unfortunately, for many of us, all the energy and enthusiasm of new ideas can soon turn to overwhelm when we think about planning and implementation. Before we know it, the excitement of a new idea has been replaced by doubt, panic or anxiety. Even fear may raise its ugly head as the steps, deadlines, and "how-to"s involved become clearer and grow into time consuming, confusing lists of details and "have-to"s. We find ourselves on a roller coaster ride of emotions and lose sight of where we were headed.

At this point it is easy to 1) get completely immobilized; 2) convince ourselves that our idea wasn't really a good idea; or 3) choose an easier path that is the complete opposite of where we want our life or business to go.

Here are three tips to help you get off the roller coaster ride and bridge the great divide between concept and goal completion:

- Take action now.
- Get the support you need.
- Be clear about your "disco ball."

1. Take action:

Putting off action will only intensify fear and despair. Take for example writing this article. Just sitting down and thinking about "what to write" made me a bit panicky.

The more I thought about it, the more my brain became twisted and caught in all of the options. So, I kept putting it off, which made me even more frustrated and panicky. I was on the idea-to-action roller coaster. It was not until I took the action of simply jotting down a couple of ideas for titles that I felt myself calm down. Even though I wasn't exactly sure about all of the details of the article, or even how long it was going to be, having a couple of titles written down gave me a direction. I had taken action, and it was in black and white. That was empowering!

2. Get the Support You Need

One of the final steps in a coaching conversation is to ask someone what support they need to accomplish the next steps they plan. Often, moving forward requires help, advice, accountability, or follow up with others. As an ADHD entrepreneur, I have learned that, at times, enlisting the support of my team helps immensely with getting me out of my own feeling of panic or uncertainty. It's amazing how much simpler a task can seem to someone else who is not wrapped up in the complexity we have created in our minds. Getting help breaking a project into steps or pieces always seems to help me get into action. At other times, I find the support of family, friends, and colleagues helpful: just talking about my ideas with someone seems to decrease my feeling of overwhelm. Asking someone else what they think about an idea gets me out of my own head. The simple fact is, building a bridge from idea to action is much easier with others involved.

3. Be Clear About Your "Disco Ball"

If you feel you are losing momentum in putting your ideas into action, it often helps to take a moment to get really clear about the *reason* this action is important to you. I call this reason your "disco ball". Clarity about the real reason for wanting to move from idea to action can spur forward movement. Our "disco ball" is what is so important to us – what drives us to take risks, spend the time, or have the courage to take an action. Simply put, it is our motivation. A "disco ball" is important because living with ADHD means that at times we risk distraction, or are tempted away from our chosen course of action, by other interesting options. Clarity about our "disco ball" helps it twinkle brighter than all of those other shiny objects fighting for our attention. To help get clear about your "disco ball" ask yourself:

- What is important to me about taking this action?
- What will this action move me closer to?
- What will it cost me if I do nothing? How would I feel?
- How will not taking this action step influence others?
- Where will I be six months from now if I do nothing?
- What positive benefits will I experience when I take this action?

Getting ideas into action can either be another chaotic roller coaster ride or, if you apply the above tips, a step by step journey across the bridge from ideas to action.

I'd love to hear your thought about bridging the divide between ideas and actions! Please write to me at support@coachingforadhd.com.

~Laurie Dupar, PMHNP, RN, PCC

Laurie Dupar is an internationally recognized ADHD coach and thought leader in the ADHD community. Visit her website to find more useful strategies at: www.CoachingforADHD.com

Help the School Help Your Child

Parents have important information to share with schools. The more that school personnel know about your child, the better they can meet your child's needs. These three tips can open communication lines:

1. Give new teachers a list of your child's strengths and challenges, as well as strategies that have been successful in the past.
2. Prepare a list of your academic, behavioral, and social concerns for an IEP or 504 meeting. Include concerns about homework, test taking, and so forth. The team should incorporate your input as plans are being written, adding the information to the IEP or 504 document.
3. Let the school know what you are doing at home to help your child. For example, mention the amount of time that you (and/or tutors) are working with your child and the specific type(s) of help given (understanding homework assignments, re-teaching the material, helping your child get started or stay focused, and/or others).

~ Roxanne Fouché

Roxanne Fouché, strength-based ADHD coach and consultant, works with, and on behalf of, students and adults with ADHD. Contact her at Roxanne@FocusForEffectiveness.com or (858) 484-4749.

Baby, Oh, Baby . . . Or Out of the Mouths of Babes

One afternoon I was babysitting my granddaughter. Wanting us to read, she said, "Go. Book." We started towards the bookshelf, but seeing a dish on a table, I stopped and brought it to the kitchen. My grandbaby said (again), "Go! Book!" Seeing the piano, we stopped and played a bit. After this, my grandbaby started wailing, "Go! Go! Book! Book!" Suddenly I realized all of the detours I had taken on the way to pick up the book!

People with ADHD have a hard time getting from point A to point B, due to executive functioning challenges and ADHD symptoms. One helpful phrase, coined by coach Joyce Kubik is, "Just because I think it, doesn't mean I have to do it." Another question to ask yourself is, "What am I supposed to be doing?" With awareness, comes choice!

Baby, oh, baby!!!

~ *Cheryl Gigler, BMed, CCC*

Cheryl Gigler is a Certified ADHD Coach and Certified Educator, dedicated to empowering adolescents and adults to experience success with ADHD. www.addjoyoflife.com joyoflifecoach@aol.com (260) 415-3412

ADHD and Vulnerability

Most of my life I believed that the definition of "vulnerability" was about being weak, about something you needed to hide and even be ashamed of. I eventually discovered, though, that the real meaning of vulnerability is about being open, sensitive and true.

Vulnerability opens up the door to deeper communication with yourself and with others. As you become more authentic, people start being more authentic with you. A whole new path of openness and honesty has then been created where there is no more hiding, no more anxiety and no need for defensiveness.

You are who you are in your uniqueness. There's no need to be normal or try to "fit in".

Gratefully surrender and give honor to who and how you are.

~ Suzanne Letourneau

Suzanne Letourneau, Lifepath Leader, excels in helping you realize the power of your story and write about it. She is also author of the award winning book *SOAR with Vulnerability*.
www.suzanneletourneau.com suzanne@suzanneletourneau.com

You Can't Have a Rainbow Without a Little Rain

ADHD is like a fingerprint. Each of us with ADHD has our own unique story. My story started in Istanbul. When I was a kid, I loved dancing, singing and acting. I believed that I was born to be a superstar and dreamed of being on stage. But my parents valued education and wanted me to go to college so I could have a decent job and financial independence.

I did go to college, in fact, I got a master's degree. I have a job that I love (though not on stage), and I am financially independent. I am a mental health counselor specializing in ADHD and burnout syndrome.

If there are miracles in life, trust me I am one of them! Sometimes I still can't believe that I finished college and got my master's degree without medication. But at that time I didn't know I had ADHD. Starting in elementary school, I had problems at school, primarily difficulty focusing. My elementary school teacher was very competitive, and almost every day I was verbally and physically abused in front of my peers because I wasn't able to answer her questions. I didn't tell any of this to my parents because I believed I deserved it. At the age of 11, I lost my self-confidence and my self-respect. I felt worthless, and I believed I wasn't loved because I was a failure.

My parents tried everything to help me, except taking me to a psychiatrist. At that time in Turkey you would never take your child to a psychiatrist for my symptoms: I was just considered lazy.

My clients always ask me how I succeeded in life in spite of ADHD. The answer is several-fold. After I started college, I stopped playing the victim game. I accepted my reality, stopped comparing myself with others, and became a solution-focused person. I learned the difference between "I wish" and "I want," and I started to take action. My motto was: "Where there is a will, there is a way." So I worked hard and never complained about it. I was ambitious and I always believed I had power inside myself. I had hope. But, my biggest drive was that I really wanted to show the world I wasn't stupid. I wanted to prove that academic success wasn't essential to succeed in life. Last but not least, I wanted to deserve my parent's love and wanted them to be proud of me. Thankfully, I was successful! But this is only part of my story.

When you are hungry for love and success, as I was, enough

is never enough. You want more and more, and you may push yourself until your mind, body and soul tell you to STOP! That's what happened to me two years ago. I had pushed myself so hard for so long that I became burnt-out. I was so burnt-out that I wanted to change my career, move to another city and start a new life from scratch. It was tough, but I did it.

Now I see my life as a rainbow, and I appreciate every teardrop in it. I don't believe I'm gifted because of my ADHD. But I believe that first my ADHD and then burnout syndrome are the best gifts that have been given to me in my life. I have learned so many things during this journey, the most important of which are:

- Don't judge yourself.
- Except who you are.
- Forgive yourself.
- Love yourself unconditionally.
- Treat yourself with respect.
- Don't worry about what others thinks of you. It's waste of your time and energy.
- When you don't know what to do, listen your intuition.
- Notice your body's wisdom. It gives you signals when you need to slow down.

- Don't run away from your feelings, it won't help you. When you really don't know how you feel about something, listen to your body. It will tell you how you feel.
- Be honest to yourself.
- Live in the present. Your past and future won't bring you happiness and success. Everything happens at this moment.
- To slow down your busy mind spend 5 to 10 minutes to diaphragmatic breathing. It will help you to overcome your anxiety.
- Don't expect a miracle, be a miracle. You have the power to do that.
- Have a balanced life.
- Don't postpone your dreams.
- Don't underestimate the power of affirmations. Repeat them till you persuade yourself. Then they will be your healer.
- Spend time in nature.
- Don't forget to exercise.

~ Pınar Kobaş

Pınar Kobaş, MS is a Mental Health Counselor who specializes in working with clients having ADHD and burnout syndrome. She also works with clients who want their dreams to come true but don't know where to start. As well as counseling, coaching and training, she is a speaker and a blog writer. She lives in Turkey and is a contributor to *365+1 Ways to Succeed with ADHD*. www.pinarkobas.com pinar@pinarkobas.com

Change is Not a One Night Stand

Change, like finding the right partner, is not something that can happen overnight. Real, lasting, and meaningful change requires time, attention and commitment.

If you want to experience and maintain any type of change, here are several factors to consider:

- **Small steps lead to large successes.** How fast you get there is not as important as consistent steps in the right direction.
- **Change requires forgiveness.** In the process of creating lasting change, you are going to make mistakes. Forgive yourself, let it go, and start again.
- **Don't go it alone.** Surround yourself with people you know, like and trust.
- **Patience is a virtue.** Give yourself time to let those small changes turn into lasting habits.
- **Take time to smell the roses.** Having made a significant change, pause to celebrate the accomplishment of staying the course and having the courage to create a better life.

~Laurie Dupar, PMHNP, RN, PCC

Laurie Dupar is an internationally recognized ADHD expert, coach, author, speaker and fierce advocate for the ADHD community. Connect with her at: www.coachingforadhd.com

To Act or Not to Act . . .?

When the ADHD part of yourself is not embraced, or even acknowledged in some cases, almost every decision is subconsciously complicated by an insatiable inner "approval hunger." In this way, it is easy to try to please others, even to the extent of compromising your own needs and desires.

Through the years, the following statements came my way, and I've chosen to make these simple thoughts part of my own mindset. As a result, I'm becoming better able to accept full responsibility for the fulfillment of my own personal, unique needs:

- Self-love is nothing more than letting my own experiences matter to me.
- I need to be courageous for only about twenty (20) seconds in order to ask for what I need.

What might become possible for you if you allow yourself to risk being your own best friend right now?

~ Sanlia Marais, PACC

Sanlia Marais, Professional ADHD/Consciousness Coach, loves supporting adults, teens and parents to celebrate their relationships by befriending their emotions and innate strengths. Contact her at: www.entreecreativechange.com sanlia@entreecreativechange.com

My Journey with Dahlia and Holly

What came first—ADHD or depression? For me, this is not a chicken and egg issue. There is an answer. ADHD has been with me all my life. Yet, it took years of anxiety and depressive episodes in adulthood before I was diagnosed with ADHD. The dual diagnosis has been a challenge to live with, helped enormously by my dogs, Dahlia and Holly.

In the spring of 2007, I fell in love with a German shepherd puppy and decided to become a pet owner for the first time. I thought seriously about what this would involve and realized that a dog would create more structure in my life and would also be helpful in managing my depression.

I named my puppy Dahlia die Blume—Dahlia the Flower. Dahlia was a great companion, with a smart and fun personality. She did help me battle my depression by providing the unconditional love that dogs are so good at. Also, I was responsible for her care, so her need to be fed and walked helped me to get out of bed and get going in the mornings. I sometimes even brought Dahlia to my therapy sessions: she was an essential part of my mental health wellness plan.

Unfortunately, at Dahlia's one year check-up I learned that she had a congenital kidney condition, and one of her kidneys was smaller than normal. Her condition was helped by a special diet (e.g., prescription dog food), medication and treatments. Still, I knew her life span would be shortened by some years.

In the fall of 2012, I knew Dahlia's time was limited, and it was unlikely that she would reach six years of age. By the end of the year, it was down to day-by-day. Then, after the holiday break, only a few days passed before I had to take Dahlia to the vet where she was eased into her final sleep.

The day after losing Dahlia, I was also terminated from the job I had held for 12 years. Due to depression and ADHD, I had experienced some work performance issues even though I had always persevered and done my best. Although I had known I would want to leave the job, and had even begun looking for other employment, the termination coming right on the heels of Dahlia's death was a blow.

Not knowing what my work situation was going to be, I had not planned on getting another dog right away. However, the fates had something else planned for me. I had been occasionally checking the local Humane Society website and, looking again, saw a posting for a German shepherd mix I had also seen the previous October. This five-year-old dog unfortunately had two failed placements. Having cared for Dahlia, I understood the characteristics and needs of German Shepherds, and, just four days after Dahlia's death, I took this dog, who I renamed Holly, into my home.

Holly immediately bonded to me and settled into her new home. I am also bonded to Holly, who got me through my grief over Dahlia's death. I cannot even imagine life without her anymore. And now, occasionally, just like Dahlia, Holly accompanies me to my therapy sessions.

~ *Jenny Bandyk*

Jenny Bandyk is an ADHD coach and consultant who supports and encourages others to understand and ADDentify their own unique style of ADHD from a strengths based perspective. She helps individuals and families better understand how ADHD can show up differently across the life span and in varied contexts. Jenny has a master's degree in child development and family studies. She also is an experienced social science, mental health and survey researcher who uses this knowledge to inform her ADHD awareness and coaching endeavors. For more information, please contact her via email at info@ADDentifier.com or visit www.ADDentifier.com

More of Others, Less of ADHD

ADHD is a mixed bag. Those of us with ADHD have many strengths. At the same time, we also face many challenges, particularly after a new diagnosis.

In the season following my own ADHD diagnosis, a pre-occupation with ADHD, and new self-regulation efforts, seemed to take over my life. There was so much to learn and to implement. So relationships of all sorts were suffering. Social graces and good relationships necessitated vigilance of speech, actions, and reactions. And I had nagging questions: Why did *I* have to work so hard at speaking succinctly, while my husband did so without effort?

Things began to improve when I realized that my self-focus and continual thoughts about ADHD were unhealthy. I have begun to focus again on whoever I am with at the moment. My joy is in putting that person first and thinking about his or her needs. Re-focusing my sphere of attention has made a world of difference!

~ Patricia Welch, MDiv

Patricia Welch, MDiv, is a late-diagnosed ordained pastor, theologian, free-lance writer/editor, wife, and mother of three adult "children."

Celebrate the Positive Qualities of ADHD

Life with ADHD is a 24-hour, seven-day-a-week-adventure!!

If you or someone you love has been diagnosed with ADHD, then you know how tempting it is to focus on the negative aspects and problems of ADHD. Less often appreciated or celebrated are the strengths or positive qualities of ADHD!!

But the amazing attributes of ADHD are **our assets** – they are the personal talents, the strengths, and the genius of ADHD that enrich our world. They include:

- creativity
- curiosity
- imagination
- out-of-the-box, innovative thinking
- humor
- musical intuition
- intelligence
- great problem solving skills
- perseverance and tenacity
- resilience
- sense of adventure

- willingness to take risks
- charm
- and so much more . . . .

Innovating Thinking

"The most successful people are those who are good at Plan B." ~ James Yorke

Innovation is about developing or using new methods or ideas in a situation. I will never forget the ingenuity one of my favorite students applied to getting himself out of bed and to class in the mornings!

Like many people in college, waking up and getting out of bed for morning classes was a nightmare. Setting alarms often failed. Having someone physically shake him out of bed was never a sure thing. So, to make sure he got out of bed and didn't miss any of his morning classes, he started his routine the night before. Each night, as he was getting ready for bed, he would prepare the coffee to automatically go off in the morning, and then set the alarm by his bed to go off exactly five minute before the coffee went off. His fail-proof innovation? The smell of coffee, you're thinking? Nope.

When he made the coffee the night before, he made sure that the coffee carafe was NOT under the coffee maker! If he didn't get up shortly after his bedside alarm went off, the morning coffee would end up all over the floor! According to him, this method never failed. Now, that's innovative!

Adventurous Spirit

"Man cannot discover new oceans unless he has the courage to lose sight of the shore." ~ *Andre Gide*

In general, adventurers are in their element when they are discovering something new or experiencing something different. When my son with ADHD was young, he was always the one who had to be out front when we were hiking along the trail, or the first to wade outside of the "safe" zone into unexplored territory where everyone else noticed the "beware of jelly fish" warning sign. He was also the first to try things like sushi, enjoy the treasures of rock hunting, and he eventually signed up for the Navy to "see the world."

I am not surprised that adventurous people such as Columbus, Lewis & Clark and other explorers are now thought to have had an ADHD brain style. Who else but a person with ADHD would embark on an adventure where the end result is uncertain, much less dangerous? Each day unpredictable, the risk of death high, with possibilities of falling off the "edges of the world," encountering strange beasts, and never returning to your homeland or loved ones? The adventurous spirit knows that with great risk comes great reward. People with ADHD are almost always at the front of the line when it comes to an adventure and the great opportunity of discovery.

Intelligence

"There are painters who transform the sun to a yellow spot, but there are others who with the help of their art and their intelligence transform a yellow spot into the sun."
~ Pablo Picasso

A third favorite positive ADHD quality of mine is intelligence. Statistically, most people with ADHD have a higher than average IQ. Since this innate intelligence does not always translate well on standardized tests, or in traditional academic structures, the intelligence of individuals with ADHD is often overlooked or missed entirely. ADHD intelligence generally cannot be measured by a GPA, standardized test scores, whether homework is turned in, or by academic standing. Rather, persons with ADHD show their intelligence in such areas as:

- An innate aptitude in math, knowing the answers without showing the steps
- Hyperfocus on sports, computers, performing or visual arts that make them masters
- Creative and productive thinking that generates new ideas, solutions and inventions

- A great sense of humor that makes connections to ideas or concepts others miss
- An innate sense of curiosity about the how, what and why of the world

Everyone's brain is different. So, too, is every ADHD brain. It's important not to judge intelligence in a narrow way but to remember these other, varied, areas of intelligence when judging the "potential" of people with ADHD.

We all have gifts and talents that look different . . . and that is a good thing. When we can appreciate the awesome ADHD qualities in ourselves, and honor these strengths in others, that will bring everyone happiness . . . and success!

~Laurie Dupar, PMHNP, RN, PCC

Laurie Dupar is an internationally recognized ADHD coach and thought leader in the ADHD community. Visit her website to find more useful strategies at: www.CoachingforADHD.com

THE T'NACI MONSTER

I never imagined that a little gold pill could change my life. Before taking Adderall, any new project filled me with fear and thoughts that "I can't." In fact, my mentor referred to this paralysis as the T'NACI Monster. The T'NACI (which is "I Can't" spelled backwards) dominated my thoughts, stifling my productivity. The more I tried to accomplish a task, the more this ugly monster roared inside my head! Like many with ADHD, my racing thoughts repeatedly told me, "I fear I can't finish it. I fear it's getting late. I fear I'll be bored. I fear it won't be good enough. I fear they won't like it. I fear I won't know how to do it." With Adderall, my anxious thoughts calmed down. Fear, anxiety, and over-whelmed feelings have turned into self-confidence, intention, and engagement. The T'NACI Monster has quieted, and my thoughts now tell me "I CAN!"

~ Barbara Ryan Hausman

Barbara Ryan Hausman is an ADHD coach, specializing in assisting students with ADHD with academic adjustment, and also coordinates learning and disability services at DeSales University. Contact her at: Barbara.Hausman@desales.edu

Homework Done √ Homework Turned In??

Arghhh! The frustration of homework done but not turned in!

It's not unusual for a student with ADHD to spend hours, even days, on a homework assignment, proudly tuck it into his or her backpack, and still not put it in the "homework in-box" at school.

This common occurrence does not reflect a lack of "responsibility". Instead, it's a challenge of "distractibility". Students have full intent to submit the homework and get credit for it, but they face any number of uncontrollable distractibility factors that can sidetrack them.

To make sure homework *done* is also homework *turned in*, encourage teachers to try this nearly fool-proof method:

Rather than a "homework-in box," have seated students "pass in" their homework. The taps on the shoulder and the shuffling of papers will clue a distracted student into remembering to add homework to the pile.

~Laurie Dupar, PMHNP, RN, PCC

Laurie Dupar, internationally recognized ADHD expert, coach, author and speaker. Connect with her at: www.coachingforadhd.com

Write Your Owner's Manual

Struggling to identify your optimum environment? It's easy if you know what you need. Einstein said, "If you can't explain it simply, you don't understand it well enough." That's our goal – understand thoroughly, say it simply.

These three assessments can help you understand yourself, what you need to thrive, and how to talk about it:

1. Acktivv Processing Styles Indicator
2. StandOut: The Groundbreaking New Strengths Assessment
3. Myers Briggs Type Indicator

Example: I believed I was unable to create learning curriculum. After reading, editing and marking up these reports, I discovered how I *can* design learning experiences:

- Talk out loud, not alone or silently.
- Jot ideas on post-its, moving them all about.
- Process with a trusted colleague.

I must move, write, and talk. Then, cool ideas appear. Increased awareness of how I work best made all the difference for me. Maybe it will for you, too.

~ Sherri Dettmer Cannon

Sherri Cannon, Certified Executive and ADHD Coach, helps you understand, communicate and leverage your strengths! Connect at: www.sherricannon.com sherri@sherricannon.com (310) 548-3623

Is Your Brain a Cerebral Ghost Town?

As we age, it can feel as though every brain cell we have has high-tailed it out of town! We forget names, misplace items, or fail to remember appointments.

How do we know if these memory slips are a sign of normal aging, ADHD, or something more serious, like Alzheimer's? Compare and consider the examples below:

Normal aging: We forget where we parked the car, but in a while we remember and can find it.

ADHD: We may not remember where we parked the car because we were distracted or not paying attention to where we parked it in the first place.

Alzheimer's: We might forget that we had a car, or even how to drive it.

While this tip gives you some examples, it is not intended to replace medical advice. If you have any concerns, always consult your medical provider.

~Laurie Dupar, PMHNP, RN, PCC

Laurie Dupar is an internationally recognized ADHD coach and thought leader in the ADHD community. Visit her website to find more useful strategies at: www.CoachingforADHD.com

"The power of "can't":
The word "can't" makes strong people weak, blinds people who can see, saddens happy people, turns brave people into cowards, robs a genius of their brilliance, causes rich people to think poorly, and limits the achievements of that great person living inside us all."

~Robert T. Kiyosaki

Autogenic Training – Your Key to Powerful, Sustainable Self-Care?

Finding a relaxation technique that motivates and energizes can seem like an impossible quest.

Autogenic training (AT) is an option that works extremely well for the busy, impatient individual. It is easy to learn, can be practiced almost anywhere, provides rapid results, and requires relatively little time each day.

AT involves six easy mental exercises focusing on various parts of the body. The exercises allow the mind and body to switch off the 'fight/flight' stress response, promoting rest and recovery. AT also increases concentration and focus, reduces anxiety, and is self-empowering.

AT has been extensively researched and has demonstrated effectiveness, but must be used with caution in the presence of certain medical and emotional conditions, so check with your doctor to be sure it's safe for you.

If you want to be more relaxed and focused, consider AT!

~ Anna Maria Lindell, ADHD Coach, speaker and founder Advance LP AB

Anna Maria Lindell, specializes in helping entrepreneurs and other high achievers with ADHD traits to understand their brains and increase their productivity. www.advancesweden.se

Five Golden Rules for Entrepreneurs with ADHD

Many individuals with ADHD are blessed with a creative entrepreneurial spirit and ideas galore! But, sometimes the follow-through is challenging. Here are five essential "golden rules" for entrepreneurs with ADHD:

1) Start with the WHY! Whatever you choose to do in business must have a meaningful and compelling purpose to keep you working on making it a success.

2) Use your strengths and gifts and consider hiring out what you find challenging and/or less appealing.

3) Keep a visual reference of your goals and objectives in front of you. Use it to plan your week as well as each day before it begins. You will be less likely to get off track.

4) Launch only one business idea at a time. It's tempting to act on too many great ideas at once, become overwhelmed and finish very little of any, or none at all. Save creative ideas in a file to return to when you have the realistic capacity to follow through.

5) Don't go it alone. Take advantage of ADHD coaching, mastermind groups, and business advisors to help you stay focused and moving forward.

~ Robin Nordmeyer

Robin Nordmeyer, Strategic Life Coach and ADHD Coaching Specialist helps families get beyond ADHD challenges to experience more success and joy in life ahead. www.livingwellwithadhd.com

The Short List

It's been suggested that starting your day with a list of the things you want to accomplish is ideal for productivity. But, with ADHD, sometimes creating that list is a huge challenge in itself, and sometimes the finished list is so intimidating, it's hard to know where to start taking action.

If you start your day with a list of just a *few* of the things you really want to accomplish in your day, it doesn't feel so daunting. And, at the end of the day, it's more likely you will have completed those items, leaving you feeling accomplished and successful. Choosing 1-5 items usually works well. To support work/life balance, think of personal items as well as school or work items for your list.

It's funny too . . . in between accomplishing the short list of items, it seems that a lot of those other things that might have been on the long list get done as well!

~ Jean M. Porto

Jean Porto, certified ADHD Coach and Resilience Coach, specializing in high school students, college students and adults. Contact her at:
www.inner-inspiration.com (703) 475-1041

Do you have an ADD "To Don't" List?

We all have an ADHD "to do" list, but how about the things *not* to do with ADHD—the things that don't work or are not helpful? What is on your "to don't" list?

Here are some "to don't"s to consider:

- Don't go it alone. Reach out and get support from other people who understand your ADHD.
- Don't ruminate. Learn that when you get in a downward, negative thinking spiral, you can stop the cycle by replacing these thoughts with "possibility thoughts," physical activity, or any other activity besides what you are doing.
- Don't pay attention to those people who aren't helpful and supportive, whether that's family, friends or professionals.
- Don't blame yourself for everything: there is more than a 50% chance that whatever happened was somebody else's fault!

What do you want to add to *your* "to don't" list?

~ Laurie Dupar, PMHNP, RN, PCC

Laurie Dupar is an internationally recognized ADHD expert, coach, author, speaker and fierce advocate for the ADHD community. Connect with her at: www.coachingforadhd.com

Change the Relationship, Change the Grade

Many times as parents, we feel like we are beating our heads against the wall trying to helping our children succeed in school. If you have tried "everything" and your child is still not responding, it's time to check on your relationship. Studies show that emotional connections improve performance in children of all ages, and especially in children with ADHD or learning disabilities.

IT'S ALL ABOUT CONNECTION

- Make the relationship your top priority! Your child is not his or her "grades".
- Get rid of guilt and shame and replace them with understanding and curiosity.
- Plan a fun one-on-one outing of your child's choosing: a time to love and connect.
- Ask yourself this question: As a child, would I feel motivated and encouraged by my parental behavior?
- Express love, and ask your child what he or she needs from you.
- Act on the answer!

~ Renee Woods

Renee Woods, ADHD coach and mother of 7, can help you learn to live life with more joy and less stress; improve performance; and win with ADD. WinWithADD.com

Getting Motivated

Many students with ADHD struggle with motivation. In fact, research shows that motivational issues and ADHD both stem from reduced action of dopamine, an important neurotransmitter in the brain.

But you can still get motivated! It helps to ask yourself:

- What things *do* motivate me?
- How can I bring that energy to the task at hand?
- What about my current task *is important* to me?
- When is it easier to do the things I don't love?
- What can I do to make the challenging stuff more appealing?
    - Break the task into pieces?
    - Race against the clock?
    - Ask someone to help keep me on track?
- How helpful would routines and schedules be to me in completing essential tasks?
- How will I feel if I get the job done? What if I don't?

Consider ADHD coaching for help in developing your personal motivational strategies.

~ Elizabeth (Liz) Ahmann, ScD, RN, ACC

Liz Ahmann is an experienced ADHD coach working with students and others to identify strengths, pinpoint challenges, clarify goals, develop strategies, and support success. For more tips, see www.lizahmann.com and www.lizahmann.blogspot.com

Focusing On Our Strengths

No matter how bright, creative or capable we might be, it's easy to get a skewed sense of who we are when we focus on what goes wrong, rather than what goes right, in our days. Many individuals with ADHD are acutely aware of their challenges but not as adept at pinpointing their strengths. Recognizing, naming, appreciating and remembering our strengths helps us build on them to support forward movement and create an upward self-reinforcing spiral of success.

"Bob" was a successful businessman who had lived through one of those weeks where everything had gone wrong, much of it out of his control. When he came to his coaching appointment, he seemed somewhat reluctant to admit that he had not implemented the things he had set out to do after our previous session.

After Bob told me about his week and all the things that had happened, I asked him what personal strengths he had employed to get through such a hellish week and live to tell about it.

He sat in silence for a while, unsure of what to say. Then, tentatively, he began with the strength of perseverance: it had helped him keep going even when every-thing around him seemed in chaos. With encouragement, Bob shared that perhaps he had also been helped by his dedication to a job well done. He then thought that possibly his flexibility and creativity had allowed him to quickly switch gears as things changed. He also realized that, likely, he was also served by his ability to maintain a sense of humor as he put out one fire after another.

As Bob verbalized the strengths that he had demonstrated during the week, he sat a little taller in the chair. He also shook his head as he shared a realization that if he could demonstrate those strengths during a week such as the one he had just experienced, he could likely work wonders when his work week was more typical. Buoyed by that aware-ness, Bob left our appointment intent on focusing on the strengths he brings to his work and his ability to perform well even when things don't go as planned.

Like Bob, we are all more successful and confident when we recognize and utilize our strengths rather than maintain a focus on the ADHD characteristics that challenge us.

Imagine the success you could enjoy if you regularly recognized your strengths and employed them in a variety of ways in your work or at school, with your family, and in your social life!

~Roxanne Fouché, ADHD Coach

Roxanne Fouché is a strengths-based ADHD coach with extensive experience working with students and adults with ADHD and related challenges. She has graduate training in special education and holds both a professional Certificate in Educational Therapy and a Certificate in Positive Psychology. She is the coordinator of the San Diego chapter of Children and Adults with Attention-Deficit/Hyperactivity Disorder (CHADD), and has been a presenter at state and international conferences for the Learning Disabilities Association (LDA), ADHD Coaches Organization (ACO) and Attention Deficit Disorder Association (ADDA). You can contact her at Roxanne@FocusForEffectiveness.com or (858)484-4749.
To learn more about her work, visit her blog at:
www.FocusForEffectiveness.com/blog

How to Raise Your "Follow-Through IQ"

Disappointed in your follow-through with projects? No worries! You can examine your process to determine where things break down.

Effective follow-through has 5 stages:

1. **Vision** – Write out the idea in detail as a "SMART" goal: *s*pecific, *m*easureable, *a*chievable, *r*ealistic and *t*ime-bound.

2. **Feasibility** – Determine what constraints or roadblocks might exist and anticipate how to overcome them. (People with ADHD often skip this step!)

3. **Planning** – Think through all the steps: the other people involved; the strategy, actions and tactics required; and a timetable for completing each step. Consider a "Plan B."

4. **Implementation** – Put the plan into action. Use flexibility in switching gears if required.

5. **Completion** – Tie up any loose ends, send announcements and thank-you notes as needed, record lessons learned and file any project documents.

Review your past projects to identify in which stages your problem areas lie. If you can't delegate those stages to others, then get help improving them!

~ Bonnie Mincu, MA, MBA, SCAC

Bonnie Mincu, Senior Certified ADHD Coach. Her entrepreneurial and corporate experience helps clients design their ideal process.
Coaching & training: www.thrivewithadd.com
bonnie@bonniemincu.com (914) 478-0071

Finding the Gift in ADD

Similar to most women who are Creative Risk Takers (CRTs), I was not diagnosed until adulthood. Reading and researching ways to help my son and my students, I realized that my own traits—including endless energy, the need to experience things to learn, intuitive sensibility (the "I just know" that we all have), an ability to physically/emotionally feel the emotions of others, multi-focus, scattered, anxious, compulsions, and overwhelmed sensations—were due to my neurological and biological makeup and unique sensitivities.

Through my own experience, and those of my son and my students, I have come to view ADD/ADHD very differently than most people. The brains, biology, and learning styles of CRTs are remarkably different. The brains of CRTs process hundreds of times faster than non-ADD brains. This combined with a very different learning profile portend an amazing shift in the way humans are beginning to learn and think.

Greater understanding of the amazingly plastic brain is assisting us to understand that children considered "learning or behaviorally disabled" are really "schooling disabled." Our present belief systems, both educational and societal, block us from bringing out each child's potential. These children are the visionaries who dream things that never were and assist us to manifest them in the world.

ADD is truly a gift. Yet, the outward symptoms we notice in CRTs often mask this gift. As the caretakers of these children with unique capabilities and aptitudes we must take the necessary steps to manage the liabilities created by the neurological and biological differences we see manifested as behavior, learning, and focusing challenges.

Through an understanding and appreciation of the unique strengths and learning styles children with ADHD have, and by managing their biological and neurological differences, we can discover how students best learn and, as a result, powerfully impact their chances for success.

Obviously, it would be it would be wonderful if there were a simple one-step solution to make everything work perfectly. But ADD, is complicated. It is a difference that encompasses neurological, biological, and learning preferences. Although drug therapy may reduce many of the outward symptoms of ADD, it may not always improve outcomes because medications don't fully impact the underlying causes of ADD or the associated learning differences.

Our greatest challenge as parents and teachers is to uncover the gift of ADHD so it may be honored and nurtured.

To effect change, your first objective is to eliminate or reduce the most disruptive aspects of ADD. From this more balanced perspective you can begin to fine tune an optimal plan that allows your child's unique genius to unfold.

Five steps you can take to set success in motion:

1. Diagnostic tests: ADD symptoms are related to food sensitivities, environmental toxins, immune and inflammatory imbalances, leaky gut, and allergies. Tests can pinpoint these imbalances.
2. Diet/nutrition changes: Eliminating foods and additives that your child is sensitive to, and assuring stable blood sugar levels are crucial.
3. Emotional and Neurological Balance: See the web-site www.naturaladdtreatments.com for resources.
4. Parenting Skills— CRTs are much more likely to question authority and often have more difficult temperaments, making it essential that you develop excellent parenting skills.
5. Discover your child's learning preferences:

> Dominance Profile Testing can determine learning strengths that can be capitalized on.

Eliminating the liabilities your child faces allows you to see his or her amazing possibilities. As a result, your child can flourish and your relationship becomes a series of beautiful memories.

~ MaryEllen Jirak

MaryEllen Jirak is a highly acclaimed teacher and award winning author. She shares proven techniques to assist you in achieving amazing high-impact results in your effectiveness as a parent, teacher, or ADD creative to create happier homes, classrooms, and lives using the fewest steps in the shortest amount of time. She is the author of *The Gift of ADD: Secrets For Transforming Liabilities Into Possibilities* (now in second edition), and *Cracking The ADD Code: Why Outcomes Haven't Changed and How They Can.* A new book, *Teaching Outside The Box: Conscious Teaching Through Connection,* is in production. See: www.naturaladdtreatments.com mejirak@earthlink.net

ADHD and Anxiety

Tips from the Trenches...

If you have been diagnosed with ADHD, at some point in your life you may have to deal with stress or anxiety. With stress and anxiety may come physical issues such as muscle aches, stomach issues and sleepless nights.

Finding your BALANCE is crucial to managing stress and anxiety-ridden days.

FOCUS ON WHAT YOU CAN CONTROL:

- Sleep habits: go to bed and get up at same time each day, and get 8 hours of sleep.
- Exercise daily: at least get outside for a 20 minute walk
- Nutrition: focus on a healthy diet
- Technology: take a periodic break
- Worries: write them down and then put them away

Doing a few simple things like this each day should help. If not, see your treating physician for help, and get the anxiety under control.

~ Shelly Shinebarger, MEd, Director of Accommodative Services, Union College

Shelly Shinebarger, MEd, Director of Accommodative Services, Union College, specializes in helping student with college level accommodations learn how to self-advocate and understand their needs and strengths. shinebas@union.edu

Never Give Up!

I was a Psychiatric Mental Health Nurse Practitioner and didn't have a clue what to do. When my son was diagnosed with ADHD, all I could think was, "I am the one who is supposed to have all the answers . . . , and I don't!" That was fourteen years ago.

That day ADHD became my world

ADHD came into my world that day. Although I had been a professional working in the mental health field for nearly 20 years, I really knew very little about ADHD. I understood the hyperactivity . . . we had lived with a restless, constantly moving, easily overwhelmed child for eight years. The "not being able to pay attention" part, I assumed, was why he was falling behind his peers academically. And, maybe impulsivity was part of the reason he didn't have any friends.

I knew immediately that the last thing I would do was give my child a medication to "fix ADHD". As far as I was concerned, it just wasn't going to happen. Like I had done with everything else in my life, I was going to learn everything I could about ADHD, and I would fix it. My son's diagnosis occurred before the age of the internet, so I began plowing through my psychiatric texts and journals. For the next five years, I read anything and everything I could about ADHD, and I attended conferences and professional seminars. We used cognitive behavioral techniques with my son, enrolled him in reading groups, tested him for food sensitivities, and stuck with a restricted food diet for a year–a diet that eliminated just about everything except bear meat (yes!) and corn. Despite our efforts, my son's hyperactivity, distractibility, and social and academic progress didn't really change, and I learned that bear meat is not easy to find!

Slowly we began to notice my son's self-esteem waning. He was in "time-out" more often and he had "play-dates" less often. When you are eight years old having someone to play with at recess is one of the most important things in your world. He didn't have that. As the months passed, we would hear his laughter less often as he spent more and more time alone.

The day that changed ADHD for us

Finally one Saturday, out of desperation, my husband and I decided to give our son a "small dose of medication" before a soccer game. My son played goalie. Not because he wanted to, but because as goalie, my husband and I could take turns standing near to him. We could remind him to stop climbing on the net; to leave the bugs in the grass alone; and when to draw his attention to an approaching ball.

My husband and I didn't tell anyone we had "medicated" our son, and we joined the other families from my son's soccer team that day, just as we had done for the past several years. As the game began, my son took his position in the goal box, and my husband took his position behind the net. Then something happened. My son did not "fiddle" with the dirt at his feet, or play with the net or try to look for his shadow on the ground . . . . Instead, he stood in that goal box, poised, with his feet firmly in the ground, his arms out at his sides, and his eyes locked firmly on the ball at the other side of the field.

That day, my son really played goalie: all by himself, with focus, with attention, and with complete determination. That day, as he stopped ball after ball from getting past, his team mates cheered him on, and other families asked if we had given our son "Wheaties" that morning because he was playing so well.

That day, my son left his Saturday morning soccer game with a smile on his face and his arms over the shoulders of his buddies. That day, ADHD became something we could do something about.

The ADHD days since

I would like to say that long-ago Saturday was the beginning of constant and continual improvement for my son with ADHD. But, I can't say ADHD is like that: some days are good, some days are not so good. Some days the medication seemed to help my son, and other days nothing helped. What did happen, though, was that his reading level improved drastically because the medication helped him to focus on the words. In less than two months from when we started the daily medication, my son's reading level went from below first grade to a sixth grade level. At the same time, he slowly began to have people to play with at recess, and his smile returned.

At sixteen, my son decided he wanted to "try it" without medication. He failed a couple of classes in high school, as we held our breath, but graduated with his class. After high school, sure that he did not want to go immediately into college, he joined the United States Navy. As I write this, my son is a communications officer on a submarine and has just learned he will be transferring soon. He was the top candidate on his base for the U. S. Navy diver's program, a program that requires top physical condition and mental attitude that is found in only a small percentage of military men and women.

I couldn't be a prouder mom. ADHD came into our lives fourteen years ago. It has taught us patience, courage, determination, perseverance, respect for individual differences, and so many other things. Despite ADHD, my son never gave up, and we never gave up on him. My advice? Don't ever give up!

~ Laurie Dupar, PMHNP, RN, PCC

Laurie Dupar is an internationally recognized ADHD coach and thought leader in the ADHD community. Visit her website to find more useful strategies at www.CoachingforADHD.com

Making Transitions Easier

For many students, transitions are tough. This is especially true when shifting from a fun activity, like playing a computer game, to a less engaging activity, like doing homework. To make transitions easier, consider these strategies:

- Clear a table or desk-top, and set out pencil and paper. Take out homework and leave it set up for later. Ideally, take five to ten minutes, before doing anything else, just to get started. Then have a snack, or go play soccer, and when you return, your homework will be there, ready to go. This is much faster way to start than coming home, procrastinating, and only later looking up homework and taking it out.
- Put on some transition music. Some students work well to background music or even their favorite songs. Otherwise, just keep the music on while taking out supplies.
- Try to minimize distractions.
- Give yourself a quick reward after each assignment is completed, such as a cookie or a five-minute phone game.

~ *Cheryl Feuer Gedzelman*

Cheryl Gedzelman is President of Tutoring For Success which provides home tutoring, test prep, and academic coaching in the Washington DC metro area. www.TutoringForSuccess.com (703) 390-9220

New Ways to Study?

Organizing and simplifying often works well for ADHD brains. Yet, the brain is complex. This begs the question: how can we best use the brain's complexity to aid us in studying? Here are two tips based on recent research:

1. Vary the environment for studying to associate new information with more contexts and, thus, embed it more firmly in your brain. Try sitting in different seats in your classroom; try varying the location of study sessions (dorm, library, classroom); or vary other circumstances (quiet/music/intensity of lights) for your study and review sessions. What do you notice?
2. Vary the approach to a subject within a single study session to aid memory and learning. Instead of just reading, read, then do some exercises, take notes, recite out loud, talk with a study-buddy, and/or make flash cards. If it works for you, you might interleave (switch up) subjects as well. What other approaches might you try?

Good luck with your studying!

~ Elizabeth (Liz) Ahmann, ScD, RN, ACC

Liz Ahmann is an experienced ADHD coach working with students and others to identify strengths, pinpoint challenges, clarify goals, develop strategies, and support success. For more tips, see www.lizahmann.com and www.lizahmann.blogspot.com

The Church Bulletin Board

Some years back I started a job at a church. I knew that the Pastor was said to have ADHD, and I had heard parishioners talk about him not being organized or arriving late to meetings. I had not told many people that I had been diagnosed with ADHD myself. But, around that time, a newspaper article was written about my having, and working with, ADHD. It included a large picture of my face!

The next Sunday, while driving to church, I wondered if anyone had seen the article. Then the minute I walked in the door, I saw the article, prominently displayed on the church bulletin board! The comments I heard were fantastic, such as, "How wonderful that you are helping people!" The Pastor's name DID come up, and people said, "Oh, you're not like him!"

I was surprised, but learned that support may come in unexpected ways, such as the church bulletin board!

~ *Cheryl Gigler, BMed, CCC*

Cheryl Gigler is a Certified ADHD Coach and Certified Educator, dedicated to empowering adolescents and adults to experience success with ADHD. www.addjoyoflife.com joyoflifecoach@aol.com (260) 415-3412

I Don't Believe in ADHD

I am still amazed when I hear people say "I don't believe in ADHD." You've probably heard it too. If you are like me, the moment those words come out of someone's mouth, every hair raises on the back of your neck, the fire starts to churn in the pit of your stomach, and your mind feels like it is going to explode. No matter how many times it happens, I am dumbfounded as to how it is possible to live on this earth and doubt the reality of ADHD.

"Not believe in ADHD?" Bear with me here . . . isn't that like saying you don't believe in the sun or the wind or the stars, or growing older . . . or love? We can't "touch" any of these either, but we know they exist because we see evidence of them. The warmth of the sun, the movement from a strong breeze, the shine of the stars in the night sky, wrinkles appearing on our faces, and the miraculous indescribable feeling of love. I often wonder: don't people understand that believing something is not real doesn't make it so?

Knowing what to say, and do, in moments when someone denies the reality of ADHD has taken me years of understanding and practice, and I have found an approach that I hope to pass on to you here.

First, it helps to understand that anyone who says ADHD does not exist is CHOOSING not to believe in ADHD. Despite the science, studies, and personal stories that support the existence of ADHD, these individuals really don't want to hear it. In fact, I bet if you tried to share evidence with them, they would argue back with proof of their own.

You see, most people who don't believe in ADHD either 1) probably have ADHD themselves, or have a loved one who does, and feel scared as all heck to take a look at that; 2) know someone who has ADHD and feel scared as all heck to think that they or their loved one is anything like that person; or 3) have just landed on earth from another planet and are really confused! When someone is scared or confused, they aren't open to learning the truth about ADHD.

So, I suggest: don't bother arguing. Avoid getting hooked by their remarks and trying to defend the existence of ADHD. Stay away from convincing, advising, or trying to get these non-believers to see your point of view. It will just be frustrating. Remember, it takes two to have an argument.

Instead, practice staying in the perspective of curiosity. Learning this has spared me from wasting oodles of energy that I have then been able to use to make a very real difference in the lives of people with ADHD. Be curious about how "interesting" it is that they don't believe in ADHD. It's almost impossible for someone to not be engaged when we are asking them about themselves or their views.

Remaining curious about how in the heck they ever came to that conclusion (sorry, I couldn't help myself), works much better to open up conversation. Practice taking three deep breaths and responding to the denial of ADHD with:

- "Really? What do you know about ADHD?" or
- "Really? Who do you know that has ADHD? or
- "Really? I used to feel that way too."

Try it! You will be amazed at how often the "non-believers" are just like we were at one time. Trying to make sense of this ADHD thing. Scared, confused, unsure.

~Laurie Dupar, PMHNP, RN, PCC

Laurie Dupar is an internationally recognized ADHD coach and thought leader in the ADHD community. Visit her website to find more useful strategies at: www.CoachingforADHD.com

"Courage doesn't always roar,

sometimes it's the quiet voice

at the end of the day

whispering, I will try again

tomorrow."

— Mary Anne Radmacher

Want to be a contributor to the next edition of The ADHD Awareness Book Project??

Do you have an ADHD success tip or strategy you want to share?

or

Is there an inspirational ADHD story that needs to be told?

If so...

We would love to hear from you so you can be part of our next *Succeed with ADHD* book!

Go to:

www.CoachingforADHD.com

or email:

Support@CoachingforADHD.com

Made in the USA
Middletown, DE
08 January 2015